7/7

All the
Silver Pennies

You must have a silver penny
To get into Fairyland.

All the Silver Pennies

(Combining SILVER PENNIES
and MORE SILVER PENNIES)

Edited by

Blanche Jennings Thompson

Decorations by Ursula Arndt

THE MACMILLAN COMPANY · NEW YORK

To the memory of my Mother and Father

ACKNOWLEDGMENTS

Thanks are due the following authors, publishers and others, in this country
and abroad, by and with whose permission the following copyrighted selections
are included.

George Allen & Unwin, Ltd., for "Sailing Homeward" by Chan Fang-Sheng
from Waley's *Translations from the Chinese.*

Appleton-Century for "The Vinegar Man" by Ruth Comfort Mitchell from
Narratives in Verse.

Appleton-Century-Crofts, Division of Meredith Publishing Company, for
"The Little Elf" by John Kendrick Bangs and "Cranberry Road" by Rachel
Field from *St. Nicholas Magazine* and "The Elf and the Dormouse" by Oliver
Herford from *Artful Anticks,* copyright The Century Company.

William M. Bower for "I Bid You Keep Some Few Small Dreams" by Helen
Frazee-Bower.

Jonathan Cape, Ltd., for "The Mirror" ("A Thought") by William H. Davies
from *The Complete Poems of W. H. Davies.*

Carl Carmer for his "Antique Shop," "The Cathedral of St. Louis" and "Slave
Quarter" from *French Town.*

Chatto & Windus, Ltd., for "Lone Dog" by Irene Rutherford McLeod from
Songs to Save a Soul.

The Christian Science Monitor for "Small Rain" by Alice Lowry Gould and
"Shadows" by Arthur J. Peel.

The Churchman for "The Spirit of the Birch" by Arthur Ketchum.

Collins-Knowlton-Wing, Inc., for "Caravans" by Hal Borland.

Padraic Colum for his "An Old Woman of the Roads" from *Wild Earth and Other Poems.*

The Commonweal for "Godmother" by Phyllis B. Morden and "To the City in the Snow" by Agnes O'Gara Ruggeri.

Constable Publishers for "Parliament Hill" by H. H. Bashford.

Coward-McCann, Inc., for "The Bad Kittens" and "The Mouse" by Elizabeth Coatsworth from *Compass Rose*, copyright 1929, and "The Find" and "The Shadow People" by Francis Ledwidge from *Complete Poems.*

A. A. Dean for "Gossip" by Lexie Dean Robertson.

Dodd, Mead & Company for "Two Sewing" by Hazel Hall from *Curtains;* "A Caravan from China Comes" from *New Poems* and "I Meant to Do My Work To-day" from *The Lonely Dancer* by Richard Le Gallienne; "The Lion" by Adelaide Love from *The Slender Singing Tree;* "From the Hills of Dream," "Hushing Song" and "The Valley of White Poppies" by Fiona Macleod from *Poems;* "Cradle Song," "In the Bazaars of Hyderabad" and "Palanquin Bearers" by Sarojini Naidu from *The Sceptred Flute;* and "Legacy" and "London Rain" by Nancy Byrd Turner from *Star in a Well.*

Doubleday & Company, Inc., for "The Child Next Door," "The Fairies Have Never a Penny to Spend" and "Have You Watched the Fairies?" by Rose Fyleman from *Fairies and Chimnies*, copyright 1918, 1920 by George H. Doran Company; "Mice" by Rose Fyleman from *Fifty-one New Nursery Rhymes*, copyright 1932 by Doubleday & Co., Inc.; "Song Against Children" by Aline Kilmer from *Vigils*, copyright 1921 by Doubleday & Co., Inc., and "The House with Nobody in It" by Joyce Kilmer from *Trees and Other Poems*, copyright 1914 by George H. Doran Company.

Constance Garland Doyle and Isabel Garland Lord for "Do You Fear the Wind?" by Hamlin Garland.

Gerald Duckworth & Co., Ltd., and Mrs. Alida Monro for "Overheard on a Saltmarsh" by Harold Monro.

Thomas W. Duncan for his "Village Portrait."

Dundalgan Press for "Hush Song" by Elizabeth Shane from *By Bog and Sea in Donegal.*

E. P. Dutton & Co., Inc., for "Fairies" and "My Dog" by Marchette Chute from *Around and About*, copyright 1932, renewal © 1960 by Marchette Chute; "Garden Song" and "The Starlighter" by Arthur Guiterman from *Gaily the Troubadour*, copyright 1936 by E. P. Dutton & Co., Inc., renewal © 1954 by Arthur Guiterman; "Shops" by Winifred M. Letts from *The Spires of Oxford and Other Poems*, copyright 1917 by E. P. Dutton & Co., Inc., renewal 1945 by Winifred M. Letts; and "Growing Up" and "Wishes" by Edna Kingsley Wallace from *Feelings and Things*, copyright 1916 by E. P. Dutton & Co., Inc., renewal 1944 by Edna Kingsley Wallace.

Florence S. Edsall for her "Stars."

Norma Millay Ellis for "Portrait by a Neighbor" and "Travel" by Edna St. Vincent Millay from *Collected Poems* (Harper & Row), copyright 1921, 1946 by Edna St. Vincent Millay.

John Farquharson, Ltd., for "Baby Seed Song" by E. Nesbit.

Elizabeth Fleming for her "Who's In?"

Georgia Warm Springs Foundation for "After All and After All" and "The Day Before April" by Mary Carolyn Davies.

Harcourt, Brace & World, Inc., for "Fog, the Magician" by Melville Cane from *So That It Flower*, copyright 1926 by Harcourt, Brace & World, Inc., renewed 1954 by Melville Cane; "Courage" by Amelia Earhart from *Last Flight*, copyright 1937 by George Palmer Putnam, renewed 1965 by Mrs. George Palmer Putnam; and "The Faithless Flowers" by Margaret Widdemer from *Little Boy and Girl Land*, copyright 1924 by Harcourt, Brace & World, Inc., renewed 1952 by Margaret Widdemer Schauffler.

Harper & Row, Inc., for "Snow Advent" by Joseph Auslander from *No Traveller Returns*, copyright 1935, 1953 by Joseph Auslander; "I Have Wrapped My Dreams in a Silken Cloth" and "Incident" by Countee Cullen from *On These I Stand*, copyright 1925 by Harper & Brothers, renewed 1953 by Ida M. Cullen; and "Proof" and "Wind Is a Cat" by Ethel Romig Fuller from *White Peaks and Green*.

James Hearst for his "Voices."

William Heinemann, Ltd., for "Cradle Song" and "Palanquin Bearers" from *The Golden Threshold* and "In the Bazaars of Hyderabad" from *Bird of Time* by Sarojini Naidu.

Hennessy and Hennessy and the Estate of Amelia J. B. Elmore for "Night Magic" from *Hearts Awake* and "Rain in the Night" from *Life and Living* by Amelia Josephine Burr.

Hill and Wang, Inc., for "Traveling Storm" by Mark Van Doren from *Collected and New Poems 1924–1963*, copyright © 1963 by Mark Van Doren.

Holt, Rinehart and Winston, Inc., for "Lincoln" by John Gould Fletcher from *Selected Poems*, copyright 1938 by John Gould Fletcher, copyright © 1966 by Charlie May Fletcher; "Dust of Snow" and "The Pasture" by Robert Frost from *Complete Poems of Robert Frost*, copyright 1923, 1930, 1939, by Holt, Rinehart and Winston, Inc., copyright 1951, © 1958 by Robert Frost; "A Ship for Singapore," "Polo Player," "To an Aviator" and "Who Pilots Ships" by Daniel Whitehead Hicky from *Bright Harbor*, copyright 1932, © 1960 by Daniel Whitehead Hicky; "A Little Song of Life" from *A Wayside Lute*, "Bible Stories" and "A Christmas Folk Song" from *The Selected Poems of Lizette Woodworth Reese*, copyright 1926 by Holt, Rinehart and Winston, Inc., copyright 1954 by C. Reese Dietrich, and "The Good Joan" from *Spicewood*, all by Lizette Woodworth Reese; "Gentle Name" and "Summer Shower" by Selma Robinson from *City Child*, copyright 1931, © 1959 by Selma Robinson; and "Fog" by Carl Sandburg from *Chicago Poems*, copyright 1916 by Holt, Rinehart and Winston, Inc., copyright 1944 by Carl Sandburg.

Houghton Mifflin Company for "The Plaint of the Camel" by Charles Carryl from *Davy and the Goblins;* "The Wagon in the Barn" by John Drinkwater from *All About Me;* and "Fringed Gentians" from *A Dome of Many-Coloured Glass* and "Night Clouds" from *What's O'Clock* by Amy Lowell.

Josephine Johnson for her "The Lightship" from *Year's End*.

J. B. Lippincott Company for "Fairies," "Moon Song" and "The Old Bridge" by Hilda Conkling from *Poems by a Little Girl*, copyright 1920, 1948 by Hilda Conkling; "Welcome to the New Year" by Eleanor Farjeon from *Poems for Children*, copyright 1927, 1955 by Eleanor Farjeon; "Animal Crackers" by

Prentice-Hall, Inc., for "A Memory" by Emperor Hirohito from *Hirohito, Emperor of Japan* by Leonard Mosely, © 1966 by Leonard Mosely.

G. P. Putnam's Sons for "About Buttons" from *Here, There and Everywhere*, copyright 1927, 1928 by Dorothy Aldis, and "Everybody Says" from *Everything and Anything*, copyright 1925–1927 by Dorothy Aldis, both by Dorothy Aldis; "Bartholomew" by Norman Gale from *Orchard Songs*; "The Army of the Sidhe" by Lady Gregory from *Kiltartan Poetry Book*, copyright 1919; and "In Flanders Field" by John McCrae from *In Flanders Field and Other Poems*, copyright 1919 by G. P. Putnam's Sons.

Alma Johnson Sarett for "Brittle World" by Lew Sarett from *Wings Against the Moon*, copyright 1931 by Henry Holt and Co., transferred 1955 to Alma Johnson Sarett.

Charles Scribner's Sons for "The Sleepy Song" by Josephine Daskam Bacon from *Poems by Josephine Daskam* and "America for Me" and "Work" by Henry van Dyke from *Poems*.

Cornelia Otis Skinner for her "The Path to Shottery."

Susan Skrine for "Grace for Light" by Moira O'Neill from *Songs of the Glens of Antrim*.

The Society of Authors for "Someone" and "Tartary" by Walter de la Mare (also by permission of the Literary Trustees of Walter de la Mare); as the literary representative of the Estate of the late Rose Fyleman for "The Child Next Door," "The Fairies Have Never a Penny to Spend," "Have You Watched the Fairies?" and "Mice" by Rose Fyleman and as the literary representative of the Estate of the late Katherine Mansfield for "Little Brother's Secret" by Katherine Mansfield.

Nancy Byrd Turner for her "Courage Has a Crimson Coat."

Union of American Hebrew Congregations for "Eight Are the Lights" by Ilo Orleans from *Within My Hand* and "A Song of Always" by Efraim Rosenzweig from *Now We Begin*.

The Viking Press, Inc., for "Goldenhair" ("Lean Out of the Window") by James Joyce from *Collected Poems*, copyright 1918 by B. W. Huebsch, Inc., 1946 by Nora Joyce; "Lone Dog" by Irene Rutherford McLeod from *Songs to Save a Soul*; "The Hens," "Strange Tree" and "Water Noises" by Elizabeth Madox Roberts from *Under the Tree*, copyright 1922 by B. W. Huebsch, Inc., 1950 by Ivor S. Roberts; and "A Tree at Dusk" by Winifred Welles from *Hesitant Heart*, copyright 1920 by B. W. Huebsch, Inc., 1947 by James Welles Shearer.

A. P. Watt & Son, M. B. Yeats and The Macmillan Company of Canada, Ltd., for "He Wishes for the Cloths of Heaven," "The Lake Isle of Innisfree" and "The Song of Wandering Aengus" by William Butler Yeats from *Collected Poems*.

Wesleyan University Press for "The Mirror" ("A Thought") by William H. Davies from *The Complete Poems of W. H. Davies*.

Yale University Press for "Days" by Karle Wilson Baker from *Blue Smoke* and "Misdirection" by Eleanor Slater from *Quest*.

The editor wishes to add a personal word of gratitude to Susan Carr Hirschman, editor-in-chief of the Macmillan Children's Book Department, and to Shirley Dolgoff for her patient, sympathetic and more than competent help in collecting and arranging *All the Silver Pennies*.

CONTENTS

PART ONE

PART TWO

INTRODUCTION

When I was a little girl, I had a picture book containing an Irish version of "The Old Woman and Her Pig." Instead of the usual sixpence which the Old Woman was supposed to have discovered as she swept her floor, she found a silver penny. The idea pleased me, and when, in 1925, I compiled an anthology of contemporary poetry for children, I called it *Silver Pennies*. In the Preface I wrote:

> *You must have a silver penny*
> *To get into Fairyland.*

So many people wrote to ask where the "quotation" came from that I felt compelled to write something from which to quote. The result was a brief poem called "Silver Pennies" which I placed at the end of *The Golden Trumpets*, a book of fairy tales. The essential stanza read:

> *If you find one you are lucky:*
> *Hold it tightly in your hand.*
> *You must have a silver penny*
> *To get into Fairyland.*

In 1925, we were in the midst of a great poetry renaissance. Everybody was writing or reading poetry and silver pennies were plentiful. The great poets of the period, both American and British, were already approaching the crest of their popularity—Edna Millay, Sara Teasdale,

Elizabeth Madox Roberts, Elinor Wylie, Lizette Woodworth Reese, Amy Lowell, Carl Sandburg, Vachel Lindsay, and Robert Frost; Walter de la Mare, Rose Fyleman, James Stephens, Padraic Colum, Alfred Noyes, John Mansfield, and William Butler Yeats. Some of their work had begun to appear occasionally in books of poetry for children, but *Silver Pennies* was the first children's anthology to use exclusively contemporary poems.

By 1938, when *More Silver Pennies* appeared, poetry had begun to decline in popularity. New poets of stature were emerging, but pennies just right for children's pockets were more difficult to find.

In these days, with science and technology dominating education, with classical literature, which used to be the foundation stone of a liberal education, so frequently overshadowed by the practical and the factual, it is more than ever important that children learn to love poetry at an early age and that they make lifelong friends among the poets. Technology is a tremendous force in modern living, but man cannot live without dreams; he merely exists, without beauty. And that is what a poem can be—warmth and color and beauty, aspiration in youth, comfort in age or sorrow, a companion for all the years.

Here, then, are all the silver pennies, shining as brightly as ever with their glimpses of strange new places, with their beckoning dreams and lifting wings. It is my hope that the children of today will love them, too; that they will want to search for other pennies wherever they may be found; and, especially, that they will learn their favorites and keep them in their hearts forever. As Sara Teasdale says in one of her most appealing poems:

> *Oh, better than the minting*
> *Of a gold-crowned king*
> *Is the safe-kept memory*
> *Of a lovely thing.*

BLANCHE JENNINGS THOMPSON

August, 1967

PART I

If you should hear a wee small knock at your door some still dark night, what would you think it might be . . . a child . . . a little Moon–man . . . or just an old-fashioned fairy? I wonder who was knocking at this child's door. It might have been a fairy.

Some One

Some one came knocking
   At my wee, small door;
Some one came knocking,
   I'm sure—sure—sure;
I listened, I opened,
   I looked to left and right,
But nought there was a-stirring
   In the still dark night;
Only the busy beetle
   Tap-tapping in the wall,
Only from the forest
   The screech-owl's call,
Only the cricket whistling
   While the dewdrops fall,
So I know not who came knocking,
   At all, at all, at all.

WALTER DE LA MARE

In olden times many people believed that there were fairies everywhere—lovely delicate little creatures not much bigger than your finger. If you have very sharp eyes, you might see one yourself some time.

Have You
Watched the Fairies?

Have you watched the fairies when the rain is done
Spreading out their little wings to dry them in the sun?
   I have, I have! Isn't it fun?

Have you heard the fairies all among the limes
Singing little fairy tunes to little fairy rhymes?
   I have, I have, lots and lots of times!

Have you seen the fairies dancing in the air,
And dashing off behind the stars to tidy up their hair?
   I have, I have; I've been there!

ROSE FYLEMAN

*Some people say that there are no fairies, but people
who have eyes to see and ears to hear can point out
any number of signs that there are fairies all around us.*

Night Dancers

Their quick feet pattered on the grass
   As light as dewdrops fall.
I saw their shadows on the glass
   And heard their voices call.

But when I went out hurrying
   To join them, they were gone.
I only found a little ring
   Of footprints on the lawn.

THOMAS KENNEDY

This poem was written when the author was only six years old. Do you think you could write one as good? Try it.

Fairies

I cannot see fairies,
I dream them.
There is no fairy can hide from me;
I keep on dreaming till I find him:
*There you are, Primrose!—I see you,
Black Wing!*

HILDA CONKLING

Did you ever know a little girl like "the child next door"? Don't you feel very sorry for her? I think that we would rather play with Mary.

The Child Next Door

The child next door has a wreath on her hat;
Her afternoon frock sticks out like that,
　　All soft and frilly;
She doesn't believe in fairies at all
(She told me over the garden wall)—
　　She thinks they're silly.

The child next door has a watch of her own;
She has shiny hair and her name is Joan;
　　(Mine's only Mary).
But doesn't it seem very sad to you
To think that she never her whole life through
　　Has seen a fairy?

ROSE FYLEMAN

Here is another lovely poem about fairies. Notice what a singing rhythm it has and in what unexpected places the rhymes come.

The Fairies Have
Never a Penny to Spend

The fairies have never a penny to spend,
    They haven't a thing put by;
But theirs is the dower of bird and of flower.
    And theirs are the earth and the sky.
And though you should live in a palace of gold
    Or sleep in a dried-up ditch,
You could never be poor as the fairies are,
    And never as rich.

Since ever and ever the world began
    They have danced like a ribbon of flame,
They have sung their song through the centuries long,
    And yet it is never the same.
And though you be foolish or though you be wise,
    With hair of silver or gold,
You could never be young as the fairies are,
    And never as old.

ROSE FYLEMAN

7

If what Nurse says is really true, what chance do you think that you will ever have of seeing a fairy?

Fairies

You can't see fairies unless you're good,
    That's what Nurse said to me.
They live in the smoke of the chimney,
    Or down in the roots of a tree;
They brush their wings on a tulip,
    Or hide behind a pea.

But you can't see fairies unless you're good,
    So they aren't much use to me.

MARCHETTE GAYLORD CHUTE

Of course if you should be so fortunate as to meet a fairy, there's nothing like being prepared, as this poem suggests.

I Keep
Three Wishes Ready

I keep three wishes ready,
Lest I should chance to meet,
Any day a fairy
Coming down the street.

I'd hate to have to stammer,
Or have to think them out,
For it's very hard to think things up
When a fairy is about.

And I'd hate to lose my wishes,
For fairies fly away,
And perhaps I'd never have a chance
On any other day.

So I keep three wishes ready,
Lest I should chance to meet,
Any day a fairy
Coming down the street.

ANNETTE WYNNE

An elf is one kind of fairy, something like a brownie,
with pointed cap and pointed shoes. Who do you
suppose asked the question that annoyed this Elf-man?
What kind of question annoys you the most?

The Little Elf

I met a little Elf-man, once,
　　Down where the lilies blow.
I asked him why he was so small,
　　And why he didn't grow.

He slightly frowned, and with his eye
　　He looked me through and through.
"I'm quite as big for me," said he,
　　"As you are big for you."

JOHN　KENDRICK　BANGS

Did you ever wonder who first thought of making umbrellas? Well this is the story.

The Elf
and the Dormouse

Under a toadstool crept a wee Elf,
Out of the rain to shelter himself.

Under the toadstool, sound asleep,
Sat a big Dormouse all in a heap.

Trembled the wee Elf, frightened, and yet
Fearing to fly away lest he get wet.

To the next shelter—maybe a mile!
Sudden the wee Elf smiled a wee smile,

Tugged till the toadstool toppled in two.
Holding it over him, gaily he flew.

Soon he was safe home, dry as could be.
Soon woke the Dormouse—"Good gracious me!

"Where is my toadstool?" loud he lamented.
—And that's how umbrellas first were invented.

OLIVER HERFORD

How do the shadow people in this poem differ from the fairies and the elves? Find some of the words that tell you. How big do you think the shadow people are?

The Shadow People

Old lame Bridget doesn't hear
Fairy music in the grass
When the gloaming's on the mere
And the shadow people pass:
Never hears their slow grey feet
Coming from the village street
Just beyond the parson's wall,
Where the clover globes are sweet
And the mushroom's parasol
Opens in the moonlit rain.
Every night I hear them call
From their long and merry train.

Old lame Bridget says to me,
"It is just your fancy, child."
She cannot believe I see
Laughing faces in the wild,
Hands that twinkle in the sedge
Bowing at the water's edge
Where the finny minnows quiver,
Shaping on a blue wave's ledge
Bubble foam to sail the river.
And the sunny hands to me
Beckon ever, beckon ever.
Oh! I would be wild and free
And with the shadow people be.

FRANCIS LEDWIDGE

Listen to this strange bit of conversation between a nymph and a goblin. A nymph is a wood-fairy and a goblin is usually a mischievous elf who likes to play tricks. What do you think the goblin wanted to do with the beads? Read the poem aloud with a different voice for each character.

Overheard on a Saltmarsh

Nymph, nymph, what are your beads?

Green glass, goblin. Why do you stare at them?

Give them me.

       No.

Give them me. Give them me.

          No.

Then I will howl all night in the reeds,
Lie in the mud and howl for them.

Goblin, why do you love them so?

They are better than stars or water,
Better than voices of winds that sing,
Better than any man's fair daughter,
Your green glass beads on a silver ring.

Hush, I stole them out of the moon.

Give me your beads, I desire them.

                    No.

I will howl in a deep lagoon
For your green glass beads, I love them so.
Give them me. Give them.

                    No.

                    HAROLD   MONRO

When we go to bed at night, we like to feel that some one is taking care of us, nearer even than Mother who may be in the next room. A little girl named Katherine used to wonder every night whether God would come to visit her in her dreams or send some of His good fairies.

For a Child
Named Katherine

God and the Fairies, be true, be true!
I am the child who waits for you.

I wait for God as I go to sleep.
I stretch out my hand for His hand to keep.
I look for Fairies where grass is deep,
And once where I heard a bell on the sheep.
The Saint who comes at Christmas-time
Is someway not so much all mine.
He surely comes, for Christmas Day,
But I never ask that Saint to stay.
He brings me beautiful things to keep,
But I liked the best the bell on the sheep.
God and the Fairies I cannot see
Are the ones that I want to stay with me.

They always stay with me through the night,
But they go just before the room is light.
It is always just God, or just Fairies, who stay,
But I never know which, nor which is away.
But once I awoke when it was dark
And something made me hush and hark.
My hand which I'd left outside the sheet
Was tucked very gently under my cheek
So I knew it was God who stayed that night—
And then I slept till it was light,
And when my hand stays out on the bed
I guess the Fairies are there instead.

I think the Fairies bring the dreams
And when I wake and my room seems
Very strange, because I've played
All the night in a woodsy glade
In my dreaming, then I know
Fairy folk have made it so—
Fairy folk who slide, they say,
Into the house on a thin moon's ray.
But always something has been there,
To fill my room with Day and air
To make one feel so sweet and wise
Before I open up my eyes.
But sometimes when it's bright and Day,
I feel alone and I must pray.
I am sure then and yet I say,
"God and the Fairies, be true, be true!
I am the child who waits for you."

LOUISE TOWNSEND NICHOLL

It was a little Irish boy who made a flute for himself
out of a reed and played a fairy tune. What do you
think he found in the fairy ring?

The Find

I took a reed and blew a tune,
And sweet it was and very clear
To be about a little thing
That only few hold dear.

Three times the cuckoo named himself,
But nothing heard him on the hill,
Where I was piping like an elf;
The air was very still.

'Twas all about a little thing
I made a mystery of sound;
I found it in a fairy ring
Upon a fairy mound.

FRANCIS LEDWIDGE

A griffin is a strange creature that we read about in fairy tales. It is half lion and half eagle and looks a little like a dragon. There is one in Alice in Wonderland, *but it is spelled* gryphon.

Yet Gentle
Will the Griffin Be

(*What Grandpa Told the Children*)

The moon? It is a griffin's egg,
Hatching to-morrow night.
And how the little boys will watch
With shouting and delight
To see him break the shell and stretch
And creep across the sky.
The boys will laugh. The little girls,
I fear, may hide and cry.
Yet gentle will the griffin be,
Most decorous and fat,
And walk up to the Milky Way
And lap it like a cat.

VACHEL LINDSAY

Which moon does this poem make you think of—the full moon, the half-moon or the crescent? What line tells you which it is?

Moon Song

There is a star that runs very fast,
That goes pulling the moon
Through the tops of the poplars.
It is all in silver,
The tall star;
The moon rolls goldenly along
Out of breath.
Mr. Moon, does he make you hurry?

HILDA CONKLING

When does the moon look like a cooky with a big bite out of it? This poem was written many years ago. What do we know about the moon now that our grandfathers didn't know?

The Moon's the North Wind's Cooky

(*What the Little Girl Said*)

The Moon's the North Wind's cooky.
He bites it, day by day,
Until there's but a rim of scraps
That crumble all away.

The South Wind is a baker.
He kneads clouds in his den,
And bakes a crisp new moon that . . . *greedy North . . . Wind . . . eats . . . again!*

VACHEL LINDSAY

*In spite of all our rockets and cameras and discoveries
in space, the moon remains a strange, bright mystery
at night and it is still fun to make up stories and verses
about it. This poem is easy to learn. Did the moon ever
play such a trick on you?*

Mockery

Happened that the moon was up before I went to bed,
Poking through the bramble-trees her round, gold head.
I didn't stop for stocking,
I didn't stop for shoe,
But went running out to meet her—oh, the night was blue!

Barefoot down the hill road, dust beneath my toes;
Barefoot in the pasture smelling sweet of fern and rose!
Oh, night was running with me,
Tame folk were all in bed—
And the moon was just showing her wild gold head.

But before I reached the hilltop where the bramble-trees
    are tall,
I looked to see my lady moon—she wasn't there at all!—
Not sitting on the hilltop,
Nor slipping through the air,
Nor hanging in the brambles by her bright gold hair!

I walked slowly down the pasture and slowly up the hill,
Wondering and wondering, and very, very still.
I wouldn't look behind me,
I went at once to bed—
And poking through the window was her bold gold head!

KATHERINE DIXON RIGGS

Conn the Fool was a queer sort of person. People said he was crazy, but he had lovely thoughts in his head. Sometimes when people are lonely and unhappy they make up imaginary stories to attract attention. This is a good read-aloud poem. Read slowly and make each word sound beautiful.

Moon Folly

(*A Song of Conn the Fool*)

I will go up the mountain after the Moon;
She is caught in a dead fir-tree.
Like a great pale apple of silver and pearl,
Like a great pale apple is she.

I will leap and will catch her with quick cold hands
And carry her home in my sack.
I will set her down safe on the oaken bench
That stands at the chimney-back.

And then I will sit by the fire all night,
And sit by the fire all day.
I will gnaw at the Moon to my heart's delight
Till I gnaw her slowly away.

And while I go mad with the Moon's cold taste
The World will beat at my door,
Crying, "Come out!" and crying, "Make haste,
And give us the Moon once more!"

But I shall not answer them ever at all.
I shall laugh, as I count and hide
The great, black, beautiful Seeds of the Moon
In a flower-pot deep and wide.

Then I shall lie down and go fast asleep,
Drunken with flame and aswoon.
But the seeds will sprout and the seeds will leap,
The subtle swift seeds of the Moon.

And some day, all of the World that cries
And beats at my door shall see
A thousand moon-leaves spring from my thatch
On a wonderful white Moon-tree!

Then each shall have Moons to his heart's desire:
Apples of silver and pearl;
Apples of orange and copper fire
Setting his five wits aswirl!

And then they will thank me, who mock me now.
"Wanting the Moon is he,"—
Oh, I'm off to the mountain after the Moon,
Ere she falls from the dead fir-tree!

FANNIE STEARNS DAVIS

In the days before electricity was widely used, streets were lighted by various types of lamps or lanterns mounted on posts. The lamplighter was an important person. He began his rounds at early dusk with his wand and little ladder and lighted each lamp by hand. Sometimes it looks as if the lamps of the sky were lighted in the same way.

The Starlighter

When the bat's on the wing and the bird's in the tree,
Comes the starlighter, whom none may see.

First in the West where the low hills are,
He touches his wand to the Evening Star.

Then swiftly he runs on his rounds on high,
Till he's lit every lamp in the dark blue sky.

ARTHUR GUITERMAN

Did you ever find yourself alone for a few moments in some place of natural beauty and feel that it belonged just to you? Perhaps you have shared such a moment as the poem describes, alone with the evening star.

February Twilight

I stood beside a hill
　Smooth with new-laid snow,
A single star looked out
　From the cold evening glow.

There was no other creature
　That saw what I could see—
I stood and watched the evening star
　As long as it watched me.

SARA　TEASDALE

A night full of stars is a wonderful thing. Can you shut your eyes as you listen to the poem and see the stately procession passing "up the dome of heaven"? There is no sound—only scent and starshine and stillness. Do you know the names of any of the stars or constellations? Which ones are topaz and which misty red?

Stars

Alone in the night
  On a dark hill
With pines around me
  Spicy and still,

And a heaven full of stars
  Over my head,
White and topaz
  And misty red;

Myriads with beating
  Hearts of fire
That æons
  Cannot vex or tire;

Up the dome of heaven
  Like a great hill,
I watch them marching
  Stately and still,

And I know that I
  Am honored to be
Witness
  Of so much majesty.

SARA TEASDALE

The Falling Star

I saw a star slide down the sky,
Blinding the north as it went by,
Too burning and too quick to hold,
Too lovely to be bought or sold,
Good only to make wishes on
And then forever to be gone.

SARA TEASDALE

This is a poem to learn by heart. Do you know the difference between a star and a planet?

Night

Stars over snow,
    And in the west a planet
Swinging below a star—
    Look for a lovely thing and you will find it,
It is not far—
    It never will be far.

SARA TEASDALE

Shut your eyes and try to say this lullaby to yourself.
Can you make up a little slow tune for it in your mind
—one that would put the orioles to sleep in their
"gypsy nest"?

Evening Song

Little Child, Good Child, go to sleep.
The tree-toads purr and the peepers peep
Under the apple-tree grass grows deep;
   Little Child, Good Child, go to sleep!

Big star out in the orange west;
Orioles swung in their gypsy nest;
Soft wind singing what you love best;
   Rest till the sun-rise; rest, Child, rest!

Swift dreams swarm in a silver flight.—
Hand in hand with the sleepy Night
Lie down soft with your eyelids tight.—
   Hush, Child, little Child! Hush.—Goodnight.—

FANNIE STEARNS DAVIS

This poem was written by a famous scholar who liked to discover and collect lovely old lost poems written by the Celts who lived in Great Britain long ago. This one is an ancient lullaby.

Hushing Song

Eily, Eily,
   My bonnie wee lass:
The winds blow,
   And the hours pass.

But never a wind
   Can do thee wrong,
Brown Birdeen, singing
   Thy bird-heart song.

And never an hour
   But has for thee
Blue of the heaven
   And green of the sea:

Blue for the hope of thee,
   Eily, Eily;
Green for the joy of thee,
   Eily, Eily.

Swing in thy nest, then,
   Here on my heart,
Birdeen, Birdeen,
   Here on my heart,
   Here on my heart!

       FIONA MACLEOD

Here is another lullaby, this time in the Irish dialect. All the mothers who live in fishing villages want their boys to be strong and hardy in order to follow the sea, but there's always a fear in their hearts when the men-folk are out on the deep.

Hush Song

Och, hush ye then, och hush ye—
    There's herrin's in the bay,
    An' you'll be the wee fisherman
    Some day—some day.

Och, rest ye then, och rest ye—
    The herrin's do be small,
    An' you're the boy when you'll be big
    Will catch them all.

Och, hush ye then, och hush ye—
    The night is dark an' wet,
    An' you too wee, och heart o' mine,
    For fishin' yet.

Och, hush ye then, och hush ye—
    'Tis cowld upon the sea,
    But this wee house is warm itself
    For you an' me.

Och, sleep ye now, och sleep ye—
    For sure a night will come
    When you'll be wakin' on the sea,
    An' me at home.

ELIZABETH SHANE

Mothers the world over sing lullabies to their children. This one comes from India. A neem *is a big tree native to that country.*

Cradle Song

From groves of spice,
  O'er fields of rice,
Athwart the lotus-stream,
  I bring for you,
  Aglint with dew,
A little lovely dream.

  Sweet, shut your eyes,
  The wild fire-flies
Dance through the fairy *neem;*
  From the poppy-bole
  For you I stole
A little lovely dream.

  Dear eyes, good night,
  In golden light
The stars around you gleam;
  On you I press
  With soft caress
A little lovely dream.

SAROJINI NAIDU

This would be a very good poem to use if you were trying to put baby brother or sister to sleep. It is rather difficult to learn because the stanzas are so much alike. It makes one sleepy just to read it.

The Sleepy Song

As soon as the fire burns red and low,
And the house up-stairs is still,
She sings me a queer little sleepy song,
Of sheep that go over a hill.

The good little sheep run quick and soft,
Their colors are gray and white:
They follow their leader nose to tail,
For they must be home by night.

And one slips over and one comes next,
And one runs after behind,
The gray one's nose at the white one's tail,
The top of the hill they find.

And when they get to the top of the hill
They quietly slip away,
But one runs over and one comes next,
Their colors are white and gray.

And over they go, and over they go,
And over the top of the hill,
The good little sheep run quick and soft,
And the house up-stairs is still.

And one slips over and one comes next,
The good little, gray little sheep!
I watch how the fire burns red and low,
And she says that I fall asleep.

JOSEPHINE DASKAM BACON

*Of course no careful housewife would deliberately en-
courage the little gray mouse as a regular guest, but
who could resist this sad complaint?*

The Mouse

I heard a mouse
Bitterly complaining
In a crack of moonlight
Aslant on the floor—

"Little I ask,
And that little is not granted;
There are few crumbs
In this world any more.

"The bread box is tin
And I cannot get in.

"The jam's in a jar
My teeth cannot mar.

"The cheese sits by itself
On the ice-box shelf.

"All night I run
Searching and seeking;
All night I run
About on the floor.

"Moonlight is there
And a bare place for dancing,
But no little feast
Is spread any more."

ELIZABETH COATSWORTH

This is an easy poem to learn. See if you can learn it by reading it three times.

The Little Turtle

There was a little turtle.
He lived in a box.
He swam in a puddle.
He climbed on the rocks.

He snapped at a mosquito.
He snapped at a flea.
He snapped at a minnow.
And he snapped at me.

He caught the mosquito.
He caught the flea.
He caught the minnow.
But he didn't catch me.

VACHEL LINDSAY

Puppies certainly can cause a good deal of trouble until they have been properly trained, but it is very difficult to scold them even when they do track up the house or eat somebody's shoes.

My Dog

His nose is short and scrubby;
   His ears hang rather low;
And he always brings the stick back,
   No matter how far you throw.

He gets spanked rather often
   For things he shouldn't do,
Like lying-on-beds, and barking,
   And eating up shoes when they're new.

He always wants to be going
   Where he isn't supposed to go.
He tracks up the house when it's snowing—
   Oh, puppy, I love you so!

MARCHETTE GAYLORD CHUTE

*In every house there are many families. You think that
your family is the only one; but if you keep your eyes
and ears open you will learn that you live in a regular
apartment house with families in the cellar, under the
porch and in the attic.*

Who's In?

"The door is shut fast
And everyone's out."
But people don't know
What they're talking about!

Says the fly on the wall,
And the flame on the coals,
And the dog on his rug,
And the mice in their holes,
And the kitten curled up,
And the spiders that spin—
"What, everyone out?
Why, everyone's in!"

ELIZABETH FLEMING

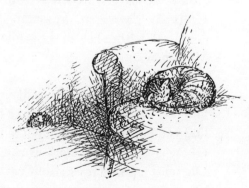

This is a "just-for-fun" poem about a proud, mysterious cat. It ought to be chanted almost as if you were singing it. Try to mew like a very proud cat indeed.

The Mysterious Cat

I saw a proud, mysterious cat,
I saw a proud, mysterious cat
Too proud to catch a mouse or rat—
Mew, mew, mew.

But catnip she would eat, and purr,
But catnip she would eat, and purr,
And goldfish she did much prefer—
Mew, mew, mew.

I saw a cat—'twas but a dream,
I saw a cat—'twas but a dream
Who scorned the slave that brought her cream—
Mew, mew, mew.

Unless the slave were dressed in style,
Unless the slave were dressed in style
And knelt before her all the while—
Mew, mew, mew.

Did you ever hear of a thing like that?
Did you ever hear of a thing like that?
Did you ever hear of a thing like that?
Oh, what a proud mysterious cat.
Oh, what a proud mysterious cat.
Oh, what a proud mysterious cat.
Mew . . . mew . . . mew.

VACHEL LINDSAY

*Not many people share this poet's opinions about mice,
although white mice are occasionally kept as pets. Do
you think "mice are nice"?*

Mice

I think mice
Are rather nice.

  Their tails are long,
  Their faces small,
  They haven't any
  Chins at all.
  Their ears are pink,
  Their teeth are white,
  They run about
  The house at night.
  They nibble things
  They shouldn't touch,
  And no one seems
  To like them much.

But I think mice
Are nice.

       ROSE FYLEMAN

This poor camel seems to think that he has a very hard life. Do you remember the story of "How the Camel Got His Hump" in the Just-So Stories? *Perhaps the camel deserves some of his ill luck.*

The Plaint
of the Camel

Canary-birds feed on sugar and seed,
    Parrots have crackers to crunch;
And as for the poodles, they tell me the noodles
    Have chickens and cream for their lunch.
        But there's never a question
        About *my* digestion—
        Anything does for me!

Cats, you're aware, can repose in a chair,
    Chickens can roost upon rails;
Puppies are able to sleep in a stable,
    And oysters can slumber in pails.
        But no one supposes
        A poor Camel dozes—
        Any place does for me!

Lambs are enclosed where it's never exposed,
    Coops are constructed for hens;
Kittens are treated to houses well heated,
    And pigs are protected by pens.
        But a Camel comes handy
        Wherever it's sandy—
        Anywhere does for me!

People would laugh if you rode a giraffe,
   Or mounted the back of an ox;
It's nobody's habit to ride on a rabbit,
   Or try to bestraddle a fox.
      But as for a Camel, he's
      Ridden by families—
      Any load does for me!

A snake is as round as a hole in the ground,
   And weasels are wavy and sleek;
And no alligator could ever be straighter
   Than lizards that live in a creek,
      But a Camel's all lumpy
      And bumpy and humpy—
      Any shape docs for me!

                    CHARLES EDWARD CARRYL

Have you ever watched hens go to bed? This poem is full of words which exactly describe the way hens sound when they are settling down for the night. Which line do you like best? What do you think the hens are asking?

The Hens

The night was coming very fast;
It reached the gate as I ran past.

The pigeons had gone to the tower of the church
And all the hens were on their perch

Up in the barn, and I thought I heard
A piece of a little purring word.

I stopped inside, waiting and staying,
To try to hear what the hens were saying.

They were asking something, that was plain,
Asking it over and over again.

One of them moved and turned around,
Her feathers made a ruffled sound,

A ruffled sound, like a bushful of birds,
And she said her little asking words.

She pushed her head close into her wing,
But nothing answered anything.

ELIZABETH MADOX ROBERTS

Some people plan their gardens especially to attract
birds and butterflies. The hummingbird likes flowers
with deep cups. The ruby throat of a hummingbird or
the frail white wings of a butterfly are a lovely sight
just above the tall blue larkspurs. Bee-balm is a bril-
liantly colored flower with a fringed cup.

Garden Song

Bee-balm for humming-birds,
　　Roses for the bee,
Larkspur for butterflies
　　And hollyhocks for me;
Blue flax for orioles
　　To mend their hanging nests,
But bee-balm for humming-birds,
　　Our ever-welcome guests.

ARTHUR GUITERMAN

Read this poem three times and you will know it by heart—and isn't it a pleasant poem to remember?

I Heard a Bird Sing

I heard a bird sing
   In the dark of December
A magical thing
   And sweet to remember.

"We are nearer to Spring
   Than we were in September,"
I heard a bird sing
   In the dark of December.

OLIVER HERFORD

The trap is one of the cruelest devices that man uses to hunt wild animals. It is bad enough to think of a lion or a tiger suffering in a trap, but the thought of a little soft rabbit caught by the paw is very sad indeed. Can you feel the anxious sympathy in this poem?

The Snare

I hear a sudden cry of pain!
   There is a rabbit in a snare;
Now I hear the cry again,
   But I cannot tell from where.

But I cannot tell from where
   He is calling out for aid;
Crying on the frightened air,
   Making everything afraid.

Making everything afraid,
   Wrinkling up his little face,
As he cries again for aid;
   And I cannot find the place!

And I cannot find the place
   Where his paw is in the snare;
Little one! Oh, little one!
   I am searching everywhere.

JAMES STEPHENS

The author of this poem feels very sorry for all animals that are ill treated or held captive. He thinks that the very angels would rejoice and ring the bells of Heaven if all the animals now in captivity were suddenly released and all the wild animals were allowed to remain free and uncaged forever.

The Bells of Heaven

'Twould ring the bells of Heaven
The wildest peal for years,
If Parson lost his senses
And people came to theirs,
And he and they together
Knelt down with angry prayers
For tamed and shabby tigers
And dancing dogs and bears,
And wretched, blind pit ponies,
And little hunted hares.

RALPH HODGSON

In this country we do not eat singing birds, but in some countries it is no uncommon sight to see them for sale in the markets. What do the birds do for us besides giving us music and beauty to look at? Why was there nothing for sale in Stupidity Street?

Stupidity Street

I saw with open eyes
Singing birds sweet
Sold in the shops
For the people to eat,
Sold in the shops of
Stupidity Street.

I saw in vision
The worm in the wheat,
And in the shops nothing
For people to eat;
Nothing for sale in
Stupidity Street.

RALPH   HODGSON

People use patterns to cut out dresses and sometimes a poet uses a pattern to "cut out" a poem. Can you find the pattern in this one? It sounds easy, but it is really rather difficult to make a poem like this. Why is it called "The Rivals"?

The Rivals

I heard a bird at dawn
   Singing sweetly on a tree,
That the dew was on the lawn,
   And the wind was on the lea;
But I didn't listen to him,
   For he didn't sing to me.

I didn't listen to him,
   For he didn't sing to me
That the dew was on the lawn
   And the wind was on the lea;
I was singing at the time
   Just as prettily as he.

I was singing all the time,
   Just as prettily as he,
About the dew upon the lawn
   And the wind upon the lea;
So I didn't listen to him
   As he sang upon a tree.

JAMES STEPHENS

Have you a little baby brother? See if you can tell in how many ways he is like this baby and in how many ways he is different.

Bartholomew

Bartholomew is very sweet,
From sandy hair to rosy feet.

Bartholomew is six months old,
And dearer far than pearls or gold.

Bartholomew has deep blue eyes,
Round pieces dropped from out the skies.

Bartholomew is hugged and kissed:
He loves a flower in either fist.

Bartholomew's my saucy son:
No mother has a sweeter one!

NORMAN GALE

Nearly everyone can sympathize with the little girl in this poem, since most of us have had the same experience ourselves.

Everybody Says

Everybody says
I look just like my mother.
Everybody says
I'm the image of Aunt Bee.
Everybody says
My nose is like my father's,
But *I* want to look like *me*.

DOROTHY ALDIS

In these days, when everybody seems to be trying to look like somebody else, it is well to remember that the most attractive people are those who look like themselves. If you could choose, how would you want to look?

Wishes

I wish my eyes were big and blue,
    And I had golden curls;
I wish my legs were fatter, too,
Like other little girls'!

I'd love a dimple in my chin;
    I wish my mouth were small—
And, oh, the way my teeth fit in
I do not like at all!

But Daddy says he really thinks
    That when I get my growth,
I'll look like Mother. "Cheer up, Jinks!"
He says, and hugs us both.

How very splendid that would be!
    I wonder if it's true—
For Mother says that she can see
I'm Daddy—through and through!

And they don't look alike one bit;
    It's queer as queer can be
That I can look like both and it
Just makes me look like me!

And when I wish my hair would curl
    And that my eyes were blue,
My mother says, "No, little girl—
For then you'd not be you!"

                    EDNA KINGSLEY WALLACE

Did you ever see a baby playing with his own toes and trying to put them into his mouth? It makes the author of this poem think of a bunch of roses.

A Bunch of Roses

The rosy mouth and rosy toe
   Of little baby brother
Until about a month ago
   Had never met each other;
But nowadays the neighbors sweet,
   In every sort of weather,
Half way with rosy fingers meet,
   To kiss and play together.

JOHN BANNISTER TABB

Everyone has button trouble at one time or another. Of course we ought to have our buttons sewed on firmly; but when they come off, three cheers for the man who invented safety pins!

About Buttons

Every button has a door
Which opens wide to let him in;
But when he rolls upon the floor,
Because he's tired of where he's been
And we can't find him any more,
We use a pin.

DOROTHY ALDIS

Growing up can be a very trying process, especially in a large family who are fond of teasing. We ought to be considerate enough not to tease in public anyway. Did you know that "bandy" means "bowlegged"?

Growing Up

I'm growing very big and tall,
Almost to mother's shoulder;
And though some things of course I like,
In getting to be older,

My legs and arms have grown so long
That father laughs and Bobby
Just grins and says, "Oh, gee, Pauline,
Your knees are awful knobby!"

And uncle calls me "Spindle-shanks"
And "Polly-doodle-dandy"
And says, "My child, be thankful that
Your lovely legs aren't bandy."

It's nice to reach high hooks and things,
If anybody pleases,
But I do wish my family
Weren't all such awful teases.

I don't know where to *put* myself
When mother tries to hold me;
I wish she knew some comfy way
To take me up and fold me.

Of course she's always letting down
My skirts and sleeves to hide me—
But, oh, I wish my bones would wait
Till I grow up inside me!

EDNA KINGSLEY WALLACE

Does your mother ever let you choose just what you will have for supper for a special treat, perhaps on Sunday evening? I wonder if you would choose what this little boy did. Perhaps you would like something else better.

Animal Crackers

Animal crackers, and cocoa to drink,
That is the finest of suppers, I think;
When I'm grown up and can have what I please
I think I shall always insist upon these.

What do *you* choose when you're offered a treat?
When Mother says, "What would you like best to eat?"
Is it waffles and syrup, or cinnamon toast?
It's cocoa and animals that *I* love the most!

The kitchen's the cosiest place that I know:
The kettle is singing, the stove is aglow,
And there in the twilight, how jolly to see
The cocoa and animals waiting for me.

Daddy and Mother dine later in state,
With Mary to cook for them, Susan to wait;
But they don't have nearly as much fun as I
Who eat in the kitchen with Nurse standing by;
And Daddy once said he would like to be me
Having cocoa and animals once more for tea!

CHRISTOPHER MORLEY

When children are very small and just learning about this interesting world, they often have strange ideas about things. Can you remember any queer ideas that you used to have?

Little Brother's Secret

When my birthday was coming
Little Brother had a secret.
He kept it for days and days
And just hummed a little tune when I asked him.
But one night it rained,
And I woke up and heard him crying;
Then he told me.
"I planted two lumps of sugar in your garden
Because you love it so frightfully.
I thought there would be a whole sugar tree for
    your birthday.
And now it will be all melted."
Oh, the darling!

KATHARINE MANSFIELD

Michael, Deborah and Christopher were real children and they did a good many naughty things, but their mother was only joking when she called her poem "Song Against Children." Can you recall any similar incidents in your own family?

Song Against Children

O the barberry bright, the barberry bright!
It stood on the mantelpiece because of the height.
Its stems were slender and thorny and tall,
And it looked most beautiful against the grey wall.
But Michael climbed up there in spite of the height,
And he ate all the berries off the barberry bright.

O the round holly wreath, the round holly wreath!
It hung in the window with ivy beneath.
It was plump and prosperous, spangled with red;
And I thought it would cheer me although I were dead.
But Deborah climbed on the table beneath,
And she ate all the berries off the round holly wreath.

O the mistletoe bough, the mistletoe bough!
Could anyone touch it? I did not see how.
I hung it up high that it might last long,
I wreathed it with ribbons and hailed it with song.
But Christopher reached it, I do not know how,
And he ate all the berries off the mistletoe bough.

ALINE KILMER

A London child speaks in this poem. What kind of work do you think his father does? Do you think the child takes his father's supper to him? Is there anything to indicate that the London he tells about is not the London of today?

Parliament Hill

Have you seen the lights of London how they twinkle,
    twinkle, twinkle,
Yellow lights, and silver lights, and crimson lights, and blue?
And there among the other lights is Daddy's little
    lantern-light,
Bending like a finger-tip, and beckoning to you.

Never was so tall a hill for tiny feet to scramble up,
Never was so strange a world to baffle little eyes,
Half of it as black as ink with ghostly feet to fall on it,
And half of it all filled with lamps and cheerful
    sounds and cries.

Lamps in golden palaces, and station-lamps, and
    steamer-lamps,
Very nearly all the lamps that Mother ever knew,
And there among the other lamps is Daddy's little
    lantern-lamp
Bending like a finger-tip, and beckoning to you.

H. H. BASHFORD

Names are very interesting. Sometimes they seem to fit people, and often they are all wrong. Did you ever look up the meaning of your own name? Some names have quite fascinating histories.

Gentle Name

Mary is a gentle name
Like the sound of silver bells,
Like a blue and quiet flame,
Like country brooks and ferny smells;
A friendly, wistful name and airy—
Mary.

SELMA ROBINSON

The name "Goldenhair" has a fairy sound. Some of the old tales use that name instead of "Goldilocks." Which do you like better? The Goldenhair in the poem was a real little girl.

Goldenhair

Lean out of the window,
   Goldenhair;
I heard you singing
   A merry air.

My book was closed;
   I read no more,
Watching the fire dance
   On the floor.

I have left my book,
   I have left my room,
For I heard you singing
   Through the gloom.

Singing and singing
   A merry air,
Lean out of the window,
   Goldenhair.

JAMES JOYCE

This is an English poem, and the word "starn" is the way some of the country people in England say "stern." Since the stern of a boat is the back, you can guess where the scarecrow has his patch.

The Wagon in the Barn

There are mushrooms in the paddock,
    And walnuts on the trees,
And a hive in the corner
    To keep the honey-bees;
There's a hay-rick in the rick-yard,
    And another one of wheat,
And there are cooking apples,
    And other ones to eat.

There are berries on the bushes,
    The yellow ones and red,
There are starlings in the willows,
    And swallows in the shed;
There's a scarecrow in the garden,
    With a patch upon his starn,
But the thing that I like best is
    The wagon in the barn.

For in the rainy weather,
    We all climb up inside,
And we have a team of horses
    To take us for a ride;
And although they think we're playing
    In the barn because it rains,
We go riding in the wagon
    For miles along the lanes.

JOHN DRINKWATER

When winter is over and the first signs of spring appear, most of us feel like going out into the woods and singing just to show how happy we are. Could you make up a tune for this little song?

The Day Before April

The day before April
   Alone, alone,
I walked in the woods
   And sat on a stone.

I sat on a broad stone
   And sang to the birds.
The tune was God's making
   But I made the words.

             MARY CAROLYN DAVIES

A little boy far away in India is telling you in this poem how he plays with paper boats. This would look more like poetry if we could see it written in his own language. Isn't it strange that in that distant land he plays games very like those that you play? People are really a good deal alike no matter where they live.

Paper Boats

Day by day I float my paper boats one by one down the running stream.

In big black letters I write my name on them and the name of the village where I live.

I hope that someone in some strange land will find them and know who I am.

I load my little boats with *shiuli* flowers from our garden, and hope that these blooms of dawn will be carried safely to land in the night.

I launch my paper boats and look up into the sky and see the little clouds setting their white bulging sails.

I know not what playmate of mine in the sky sends them down the air to race with my boats!

When night comes I bury my face in my arms and dream that my paper boats float on and on under the midnight stars.

The fairies of sleep are sailing in them, and the lading is their baskets full of dreams.

RABINDRANATH TAGORE

The writer of this poem has an interesting idea. Who are some of the other "little brown brothers" waking down there in the dark?

Baby Seed Song

Little brown brother, oh! little brown brother,
    Are you awake in the dark?
Here we lie cosily, close to each other:
    Hark to the song of the lark—
"Waken!" the lark says, "waken and dress you;
    Put on your green coats and gay,
Blue sky will shine on you, sunshine caress you—
    Waken! 'tis morning—'tis May!"

Little brown brother, oh! little brown brother,
    What kind of a flower will you be?
I'll be a poppy—all white, like my mother;
    Do be a poppy like me.
What! You're a sunflower! How I shall miss you
    When you're grown golden and high!
But I shall send all the bees up to kiss you;
    Little brown brother, good-bye.

E. NESBIT

Who are the little folks in the grass? Whose houses might we pull down "roof and all" by stepping carelessly?

Little Folks in the Grass

In the grass
A thousand little people pass,
And all about a myriad little eyes look out,
For there are houses every side
Where the little folks abide,
Where the little folks take tea
On a grass blade near a tree;
Where they hold their Sabbath meetings,
Pass each other, giving greetings,
So remember when you pass
Through the grass;
Little folks are everywhere;
Walk quite softly, take great care
Lest you hurt them unaware,
Lest the giant that is YOU
Pull a house down with his shoe,
Pull a house down, roof and all,
Killing children, great and small;
So the wee eyes look at you
As you walk the meadows through;
So remember when you pass
Through the grass.

ANNETTE WYNNE

Wouldn't you like to go out to the pasture too and help clean the spring and see the little baby calf?

The Pasture

I'm going out to clean the pasture spring;
I'll only stop to rake the leaves away
(And wait to watch the water clear, I may):
I sha'n't be gone long.—You come too.

I'm going out to fetch the little calf
That's standing by the mother. It's so young
It totters when she licks it with her tongue.
I sha'n't be gone long.—You come too.

ROBERT FROST

Things never seem quite the same at night, do they?
Can you think of some other things that surprise you
in the dark which the little boy in the poem has not
told about?

Night Magic

(A Lie-Awake Song)

The apples falling from the tree
Make such a heavy bump at night
I always am surprised to see
They are so little, when it's light;

And all the dark just sings and sings
So loud, I cannot see at all
How frogs and crickets and such things
That make the noise, can be so small.

Then my own room looks larger, too—
Corners so dark and far away—
I wonder if things really do
Grow up at night and shrink by day?

For I dream sometimes, just as clear,
I'm bigger than the biggest men—
Then mother says, "Wake up, my dear!"
And I'm a little boy again.

AMELIA JOSEPHINE BURR

If there were no winter, we could never know the
wonderful thrill that comes when we hear the first
sounds of spring. We hear spring before we see it,
probably because the birds know spring is coming
long before we do.

I Heard It
in the Valley

I heard it in the valley,
I heard it in the glen;
Listen, children, surely, surely
Spring is coming back again!

I heard it in the valley,
I heard it on the hill,
I heard it where the bare trees stand,
Very brave and still.

I heard it in the valley—
I heard the waters start,
I heard it surely, surely,
I heard it in my heart!

ANNETTE WYNNE

What time of year does this poem tell about? How do we usually feel in the spring? The poet must have felt just as we do when we begin to get very tired of school and long for vacation.

I Meant to
Do My Work To-day

I meant to do my work to-day—
    But a brown bird sang in the apple-tree,
And a butterfly flitted across the field,
    And all the leaves were calling me.

And the wind went sighing over the land,
    Tossing the grasses to and fro,
And a rainbow held out its shining hand—
    So what could I do but laugh and go?

RICHARD LE GALLIENNE

Have you ever seen fringed gentians? They are shy
flowers, a beautiful blue in color, and they fade very
quickly if you bring them into the house.

Fringed
Gentians

Near where I live there is a lake
As blue as blue can be; winds make
It dance as they go blowing by.
I think it curtseys to the sky.

It's just a lake of lovely flowers,
And my Mamma says they are ours,
But they are not like those we grow
To be our very own, you know.

We have a splendid garden, there
Are lots of flowers everywhere;
Roses, and pinks, and four o'clocks,
And hollyhocks, and evening stocks.

Mamma lets us pick them, but never
Must we pick any gentians—ever!
For if we carried them away
They'd die of homesickness that day.

AMY LOWELL

Do you know the pretty white flower called Queen Anne's lace (it is really a weed) which grows along the roadside in the summer time? This is the tale of how it came there. Do you know any other name for Queen Anne's lace?

Queen Anne's Lace

Queen Anne, Queen Anne, has washed her lace
  (She chose a summer's day)
And hung it in a grassy place
  To whiten, if it may.

Queen Anne, Queen Anne, has left it there,
  And slept the dewy night;
Then waked, to find the sunshine fair,
  And all the meadows white.

Queen Anne, Queen Anne, is dead and gone
  (She died a summer's day),
But left her lace to whiten on
  Each weed-entangled way!

MARY LESLIE NEWTON

There are some kinds of trees which seem to us almost
as if they were people. We feel like giving them names
of their own. The apple tree seems particularly human.
What kind of tree do you think this one was?

Strange Tree

Away beyond the Jarboe house
I saw a different kind of tree.
Its trunk was old and large and bent,
And I could feel it look at me.

The road was going on and on
Beyond to reach some other place.
I saw a tree that looked at me,
And yet it did not have a face.

It looked at me with all its limbs;
It looked at me with all its bark.
The yellow wrinkles on its sides
Were bent and dark.

And then I ran to get away,
But when I stopped and turned to see,
The tree was bending to the side
And leaning out to look at me.

ELIZABETH MADOX ROBERTS

Does this poem make you think of any time when you have played by yourself beside the water? What do you think the water says?

Water Noises

When I am playing by myself,
And all the boys are lost around,
Then I can hear the water go;
It makes a little talking sound.

Along the rocks below the tree,
I see it ripple up and wink;
And I can hear it saying on,
"And do you think? And do you think?"

A bug shoots by that snaps and ticks,
And a bird flies up beside the tree
To go into the sky to sing.
I hear it say, "Killdee, killdee!"

Or else a yellow cow comes down
To splash a while and have a drink.
But when she goes I still can hear
The water say, "And do you think?"

ELIZABETH MADOX ROBERTS

This is a very interesting word picture of fog. Read it aloud slowly, thinking the picture in your mind, so that if those listening to you shut their eyes they will see the gray fog creeping over the land.

Fog

The fog comes
on little cat feet.

It sits looking
over harbor and city
on silent haunches
and then moves on.

CARL SANDBURG

Here is a poem about a little girl who thinks that some of the flowers in her garden are very incorrectly named. Can you think of any other flowers that do not live up to their names?

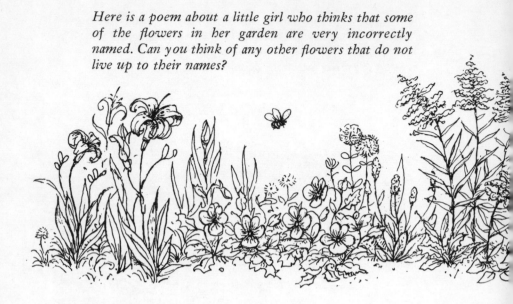

The Faithless Flowers

I went this morning down to where the Johnny-Jump-Ups
    grow
Like naughty purple faces nodding in a row.
I stayed 'most all the morning there—I sat down on a stump
And watched and watched and watched them—and they
    never gave a jump!

And Golden Glow that stands up tall and yellow by
    the fence,
It doesn't glow a single bit—it's only just pretence—
I ran down after tea last night to watch them in the dark—
I had to light a match to see; they didn't give a spark!

And then the Bouncing Bets don't bounce—I tried them
    yesterday,

I picked a big pink bunch down in the meadow where
    they stay,
I took a piece of string I had and tied them in a ball,
And threw them down as hard as hard—they never
    bounced at all!

And Tiger Lilies may look fierce, to meet them all alone,
All tall and black and yellowy and nodding by a stone,
But they're no more like tigers than the dogwood's
    like a dog,
Or bulrushes are like a bull or toadwort like a frog!

I like the flowers very much—they're pleasant as can be
For bunches on the table, and to pick and wear and see,
But still it doesn't seem quite fair—it does seem very queer—
They don't do what they're named for—not at any
    time of year!

                   MARGARET WIDDEMER

*Did you ever watch the darkness creeping slowly,
slowly along the sky and the grass until you almost
thought that it was a real person? Perhaps, like this
child, you feel more comfortable indoors with a light
which the blackness cannot cover.*

Check

The night was creeping on the ground;
She crept and did not make a sound
Until she reached the tree, and then
She covered it, and stole again
Along the grass beside the wall.

I heard the rustle of her shawl
As she threw blackness everywhere
Upon the sky and ground and air,
And in the room where I was hid:
But no matter what she did
To everything that was without
She could not put my candle out.

So I stared at the night, and she
Stared back solemnly at me.

JAMES STEPHENS

"Meditate on beauty." Another poet tells us the same thing elsewhere in this book when she speaks of the "safe-kept memory of a lovely thing." Cherish beauty, and it shall be doubled. What lovely things have you "safe-kept" in your memory?

Reflection

Beauty is a lily,
Sparkling and cool,
Its bowl of dewy petals
Stemming in a pool.

Meditate on beauty,
Hold it, and look!—
Beauty shall be doubled,—
A lily in a brook.

LEW SARETT

Here is a curious fancy about the stars. One sun, one moon—but how lavish the Creator was with stars! Before He made man, He filled the heavens with stars that man might see and wonder.

Stars

And then
He made the stars also.
What a gesture!
What a lovely after-thought!
He made them on a whim,
A tiny fancy.

With trembling eagerness
And all absorbed,
Carelessly profligate,
He made stars by the hundred million thousands,
Like grains of golden pollen.

Then, when He had done, He dropped
Into a maker's dream,
For in His mind was growing
The strange whim of man.

Goldenly slipped from His dreaming hands,
Worlds fell,
As coins through the fingers of a spendthrift.

FLORENCE S. EDSALL

This little child is going to have a good time after the rain. Can you read the poem so that it sounds "sometimes loud, sometimes soft, just like a song"?

Rain in the Night

Raining, raining,
  All night long;
Sometimes loud, sometimes soft,
  Just like a song.

There'll be rivers in the gutters
  And lakes along the street.
It will make our lazy kitty
  Wash his little dirty feet.

The roses will wear diamonds
  Like kings and queens at court;
But the pansies all get muddy
  Because they are so short.

I'll sail my boat to-morrow
  In wonderful new places,
But first I'll take my watering-pot
  And wash the pansies' faces.

AMELIA JOSEPHINE BURR

Poets have compared the wind to a great variety of things, but comparing it to a cat is something new. Have you ever heard the wind lash its tail or purr?

Wind Is a Cat

Wind is a cat
   That prowls at night,
Now in a valley,
   Now on a height,

Pouncing on houses
   Till folks in their beds
Draw all the covers
   Over their heads.

It sings to the moon,
   It scratches at doors;
It lashes its tail
   Around chimneys and roars.

It claws at the clouds
   Till it fringes their silk;
It laps up the dawn
   Like a saucer of milk;

Then, chasing the stars
   To the tops of the firs,
Curls down for a nap
   And purrs and purrs.

ETHEL ROMIG FULLER

Brittle World

Brittle the snow on the gables,
  The sleet-hung pines, the night
Sprinkled with stars that quiver
  Over the waste of white.

Fragile the earth in the moonlight,
  The glassy sheet of lake;
If I tapped it with a hammer,
  The brittle world would break.

LEW SARETT

Don't you enjoy the names of London streets? Remember "Pippin Hill" in the Mother Goose book, and "The Boy Who Lived in Pudding Lane"?

London Rain

When it rained in Devon,
Salt was on my lips;
I leaned against a gray wharf
And dreamed of old ships.

When it rained in Yorkshire,
I tarried indoors
And heard the weather calling
Up and down the moors.

But when it rained in London,
I couldn't stay still;
My feet, before I told them,
Had run to Pippin Hill.

Before I even knew it,
As wet as sops, my feet
Were splashing Dark Horse Alley
And Pickled Herring Street.

Through Pudding Court I paddled,
I waded Honey Lane—
The rain that falls on London
Is not like other rain.

Wet days are wild in Cornwall,
In Kent they're sweet and slow,
But when it rains in London,
Ah, when it rains in London,
You're drenched with long ago.

NANCY BYRD TURNER

*Rain often begins with a sharp patter, but snow usually
comes very softly. Can you see the picture—the wind
brushing up the clouds, the brook held down by ice,
and then the sudden coming of the "white bees of the
moon"?*

Snow Advent

The clouds were all brushed up and back
The wrong way by the wind;
The trees were attitudes in black;
The brooks were disciplined.

Then soft as spider on a shelf,
Or satin mouse at birth,
Or as a pigeon lends itself
Reluctantly to earth—

No louder than the silken sound
Of the web's silver wheel,
Spraying the darkness all around
With spokes of silken steel—

As soft and softer than all these
Parted the sky at noon;
And the air stood up league-deep in bees,
The white bees of the moon.

JOSEPH AUSLANDER

Hilda Conkling wrote this poem when she knew a good many unusual words but was still too little to spell or write them. Her mother used to write her poems in a notebook for her.

The Old Bridge

The old bridge has a wrinkled face.
He bends his back
For us to go over.
He moans and weeps
But we do not hear.
Sorrow stands in his face
For the heavy weight and worry
Of people passing.
The trees drop their leaves into the water;
The sky nods to him.
The leaves float down like small ships
On the blue surface
Which is the sky.
He is not always sad;
He smiles to see the ships go down
And the little children
Playing on the river banks.

HILDA CONKLING

This is a fine poem for pantomime. Choose three dancers and a reader who can chant the lines with even rhythm. The dancers begin at Part II. The waiters juggle their trays, the dancers follow directions with stiff arms and legs, dancing around the Irish lady. At Part III the sweet potato begins to dance. Then slow down the reading gradually to the very last word.

The Potatoes' Dance

(*A Poem Game*)

I

"Down cellar," said the cricket,
"Down cellar," said the cricket,
"Down cellar," said the cricket,
"I saw a ball last night,
In honor of a lady,
In honor of a lady,
In honor of a lady,
Whose wings were pearly white.
The breath of bitter weather,
The breath of bitter weather,
The breath of bitter weather,
Had smashed the cellar pane.
We entertained a drift of leaves,
We entertained a drift of leaves,
We entertained a drift of leaves,
And then of snow and rain.
But we were dressed for winter,
But we were dressed for winter
But we were dressed for winter,

And loved to hear it blow
In honor of the lady,
In honor of the lady,
In honor of the lady,
Who makes potatoes grow,
Our guest the Irish lady,
The tiny Irish lady,
The airy Irish lady,
Who makes potatoes grow.

II

"Potatoes were the waiters,
Potatoes were the waiters,
Potatoes were the waiters,
Potatoes were the band,
Potatoes were the dancers
Kicking up the sand,
Kicking up the sand,
Kicking up the sand,
Potatoes were the dancers
Kicking up the sand.
Their legs were old burnt matches,
Their legs were old burnt matches,
Their legs were old burnt matches,
Their arms were just the same.
They jigged and whirled and scrambled,

Jigged and whirled and scrambled,
Jigged and whirled and scrambled,
In honor of the dame,
The noble Irish lady
Who makes potatoes dance,
The witty Irish lady,
The saucy Irish lady,
The laughing Irish lady
Who makes potatoes prance.

III

"There was just one sweet potato.
He was golden brown and slim.
The lady loved his dancing,
The lady loved his dancing,
The lady loved his dancing,
She danced all night with him,
She danced all night with him.
Alas, he wasn't Irish.
So when she flew away,
They threw him in the coalbin,
And there he is to-day,
Where they cannot hear his sighs
And his weeping for the lady,
The glorious Irish lady,
The beauteous Irish lady,
Who
Gives
Potatoes
Eyes."

VACHEL LINDSAY

*Here is a lilting little poem that almost makes you
dance a jig. Did you ever make a whistle of a willow
twig or a hollow reed?*

Irish

My father and mother were Irish,
And I am Irish, too;
I pipe you my bag of whistles,
And it is Irish, too.
I will sing with you in the morning,
And play with you at noon,
And dance with you in the evening
To a little Irish tune.
For my father and mother were Irish,
And I am Irish, too;
And here is my bag of whistles,
For it is Irish, too.

EDWARD J. O'BRIEN

Hallowe'en

Bolt and bar the front door,
    Draw the curtains tight;
Wise folk are in before
    Moon-rise to-night.

Hallowe'en, Hallowe'en,
    Chestnuts to roast,
A gift for the fairy,
    A prayer for the ghost.

Who will have their fate told,
    This night is known,
Whose hand is full of gold,
    Who goes alone.

Hallowe'en, Hallowe'en,
    Snapdragon blue,
A lover for me
    And a fortune for you.

Stars shiver blue and green,
　　Moon's wide and white;
There, tattered clouds between,
　　Witches take flight.

　　Hallowe'en, Hallowe'en,
　　　　Apples a-bob,
　　Elves at the keyhole
　　　　And imps on the hob.

"Twelve," calls the deep bell
　　To the hollow night.
"Twelve," whisper steeple tops
　　Far out of sight.

　　Hallowe'en, Hallowe'en,
　　　　Fires burn high.
　　Who shall say certainly,
　　　　Who can tell truthfully,
　　What solemn company
　　　　Passes through the sky?

　　　　　　　　MOLLY CAPES

When you grow older and have children of your own, some of your happiest memories may well be of the times when your mother opened the big Bible and told you the lovely old tales of David, the shepherd boy, and of the carpenter's shop in Nazareth.

Bible Stories

The room was low and small and kind;
   And in its cupboard old,
The shells were set out to my mind;
   The cups I loved with rims of gold.

Then, with that good gift which she had,
   My mother showed at will,
David, the ruddy Syrian lad,
   With his few sheep upon a hill;

A shop down a rude country street,
    The chips strewn on the floor,
And faintly keen across the heat;
    The simple kinsfolk at the door;

Mary amid the homely din,
    As slim as violet;
The little Jesus just within,
    About His father's business set.

My mother rose, and then I knew
    As she stood smiling there,
Her gown was of that gentle blue
    Which she had made the Virgin wear.

How far the very chairs were grown!
    The gilt rose on each back,
Into a Syrian rose was blown,
    And not our humble gold and black.

That week long, in our acres old,
    Lad David did I see;
From out our cups with rims of gold,
    The little Jesus supped with me.

LIZETTE WOODWORTH REESE

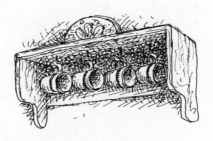

What a fortunate old lady was Godmother! Wouldn't it be convenient to have three faces—or even two? This old lady would probably be a pleasant person to meet at a party.

Godmother

There was an old lady
Who had three faces,
One for everyday,
And one for wearing places—
To meetings and parties,
Dull places like that—
A face that looked well
With a grown-up hat.

But she carried in her pocket
The face of an elf,
And she'd clap it on quick
When she felt like herself.
Sitting in the parlor
Of somebody's house,
She'd reach in her pocket
Sly as a mouse . . .
And there in the corner,
Sipping her tea,
Was a laughing elf-woman
Nobody could see!

PHYLLIS B. MORDEN

It is no wonder that a black cat is supposed to be a witch's favorite companion. If there is anything that looks like a goblin, it is a black cat with its green eyes shining in the dark. Do you ever suspect your cat of keeping tryst with goblins? What is a tryst?

The Bad Kittens

You may call, you may call,
But the little black cats won't hear you;
The little black cats are maddened
By the bright green light of the moon.
They are running and whirling and hiding,
They are wild who were once so confiding,
They are mad when the moon is riding—
You will not catch the kittens soon!

They care not for saucers of milk;
They care not for pillows of silk;
Your softest, crooningest call
Means less than the buzzing of flies.
They are seeing more than you see,
They are hearing more than you hear,
And out of the darkness they peer,
With a goblin light in their eyes!

ELIZABETH COATSWORTH

Shepherds and their quiet flocks seem always to lead a peaceful life. Perhaps they are especially blessed because they are hospitable and kind to the stranger and the wayfarer. This poem is written in the style of an old English Christmas carol.

A Christmas Folk Song

The little Jesus came to town;
The wind blew up, the wind blew down;
Out in the street the wind was bold;
Now who would house Him from the cold?

Then opened wide the stable door,
Fair were the rushes on the floor;
The Ox put forth a hornèd head:
"Come, little Lord, here make Thy bed."

Up rose the Sheep were folded near;
"Thou Lamb of God, come, enter here."
He entered there to rush and reed,
Who was the Lamb of God indeed.

The little Jesus came to town;
With ox and sheep He laid Him down;
Peace to the byre, peace to the fold,
For that they housed Him from the cold!

LIZETTE WOODWORTH REESE

In olden England the children who went from door to door singing Christmas carols were called "waits." Wherever they stopped the people gave them food and presents. The word "good-den" means "Good greeting" or "God's blessing."

Wait's Carol

Give ye good-den,
Sweet gentlemen,
   And comely ladies, too.
Give ye good-den,
For once again
   The Lord Christ comes to you.

By moor and street,
His holy feet
   Shall pass upon the way,
And give good-den
To beasts and men,
   For this is Christmas Day.

Ye gentle poor,
Set wide the door
   So He may enter in.
Bring cup and plate
With simple state,
   And let the feast begin.

And ye who hold
The purse of gold,
   Come out and spend and pray,
And give good-den
To beggar men
   For that it's Christmas Day.

BARBARA YOUNG

Christmas morning is usually one of the happiest times of the whole year. We feel so gay and contented that our happiness spills over onto everyone else. It's a pity that the feeling doesn't always last longer, isn't it?

I'm Wishing
the Whole World Christmas

I'm wishing the whole world Christmas—
The children, the beasts, and the birds;
I'm wishing the whole world Christmas—
And I'd like to have magical words
To wish just the shining wish I would wish
In the Christmas words I would say,
For I'm wishing the whole world Christmas,
And joy on Christmas Day.

O, I'd need a pen to write golden,
The goldenest pen indeed,
To wish the whole world Christmas
For the happy children to read.
I'm wishing the whole world Christmas
And may the dear Lord be kind,
And send blessings down like snowflakes
For all of His children to find. . . .

ANNETTE WYNNE

Here is a poem that has a great deal of meaning if we look for it. What are some of the things in the world that are in "a muddle"? What kind of new broom do we need—and how nimble and keen are you going to be about wielding it?

Welcome to the New Year

Hey, my lad, ho, my lad!
　Here's a New Broom.
Heaven's your housetop
　And Earth is your room.

Tuck up your shirtsleeves,
　There's plenty to do—
Look at the muddle
　That's waiting for you!

Dust in the corners
　And dirt on the floor,
Cobwebs still clinging
　To window and door.

Hey, my lad! ho, my lad!
　Nimble and keen—
Here's your New Broom, my lad!
　See you sweep clean.

ELEANOR FARJEON

*Here is a very little poem all about wishes. Where do
your wishes build their nests?*

A Wish Is
Quite a Tiny Thing

A wish is quite a tiny thing
Just like a bird upon the wing,
It flies away all fancy free
And lights upon a house or tree;
It flies across the farthest air,
And builds a safe nest anywhere.

ANNETTE WYNNE

PART II

This poem is a charming little whimsey that tells us how Spring's lovely clothes are made. It is a good poem to remember on a rainy day when you are impatient because the rain is keeping you indoors.

Two Sewing

The wind is sewing with needles of rain;
With shining needles of rain
It stitches into the thin
Cloth of earth—in,
In, in, in.

Oh, the wind has often sewed with me!—
One, two, three.

Spring must have fine things
To wear, like other springs.
Of silken green the grass must be
Embroidered. *One and two and three.*

Then every crocus must be made
So subtly as to seem afraid
Of lifting color from the ground;
And after crocuses, the round
Heads of tulips and all the fair
Intricate garb that Spring will wear.
The wind must sew with needles of rain,
With shining needles of rain
Stitching into the thin
Cloth of earth—in,
In, in, in—
For all the springs of futurity.
One, two, three.

HAZEL HALL

There are a great many kinds of people in the world and luckily they do not all like the same things. Some people enjoy stormy weather and others like the quiet rainy days when one may stay indoors and read or play. We all like the kind of person in this poem who is not frightened or excited in time of trouble, a quiet, home-loving person whom neither "hell nor heaven" can surprise.

Who Loves the Rain

Who loves the rain
And loves his home,
And looks on life with quiet eyes,
Him will I follow through the storm;
And at his hearth-fire keep me warm;
Nor hell nor heaven shall that soul surprise,
Who loves the rain,
And loves his home,
And looks on life with quiet eyes.

FRANCES SHAW

Someone said that the ten loveliest words in the language are these: lullaby, tranquil, murmur, chimes, melody, glisten, luminous, golden, mist, dawn. This poet thought that it would be an interesting experiment to weave them into a sonnet. Here is the result. Make a list of lovely words yourself. Perhaps you could even make them into a poem. Some words appeal to the ear and some to the eye, and some we like for their meaning. You may want to make three different lists.

Small Rain

No lullaby is older than the rain:
The small rain falling on the tender grass.
The Hebrew shepherd lad, the Lesbian lass,
Hushed by its tranquil murmuring have lain
And dreamed their dreams. The nations rise and wane,
The destinies of men and empires pass;
But still tonight upon my window glass
Thin chimes tap out their slumber-song again.

I hear it falling, falling through the night—
The ancient rain that makes the worn earth new—
Knowing that when both rain and night are gone,
Most gently will the fingers of first light
Wake birds to melody, and glisten through
The luminous and golden mist of dawn.

ALICE LAWRY GOULD

In these days when automation has eliminated much hard physical labor and wheels have largely supplanted legs, we are all in danger of growing lazy and "soft." Have you ever spent a holiday in the woods or the mountains? How do Scouts learn to cope with bad weather and primitive conditions?

Do You Fear the Wind?

Do you fear the force of the wind,
The slash of the rain?
Go face them and fight them,
Be savage again.
Go hungry and cold like the wolf,
Go wade like the crane:
The palms of your hands will thicken,
The skin of your cheek will tan,
You'll grow ragged and weary and swarthy,
But you'll walk like a man!

HAMLIN GARLAND

Here are wind and rain in a menacing mood. There are good descriptions here—"black with the speeding storm," "a swift dark wind." You can almost feel the steaming heat and then the sharp cool wind.

Traveling Storm

The sky above us here is open again.
The sun comes hotter, and the shingles steam,
The trees are done with dripping, and the hens
Bustle among bright pools to pick and drink.
But east and south are black with the speeding storm.
That thunder, low and far, remembering nothing,
Gathers a new world under it and growls,
Worries, strikes, and is gone. Children at windows
Cry at the rain, it pours so heavily down,
Drifting across the yard till the sheds are gray.
A county farther on, the wind is all—
A swift dark wind that turns the maples pale,
Ruffles the hay, and spreads the swallows' wings.
Horses, suddenly restless, are unhitched,
And men, with glances upward, hurry in;
Their overalls blow full and cool; they shout;
Soon they will lie in barns and laugh at the lightning.
Another county yet, and the sky is still;
The air is fainting; women sit with fans
And wonder when a rain will come that way.

MARK VAN DOREN

There is a springlike lilt to this poem with its double rhymes and tiptilting cadences. Spring makes the poets pipe gay little songs.

Out in the Wood

Out in the wood today, oh, such a wonder!
Greenery over and greenery under;
Rustle of leaves with their tremulous tracery;
Swaying of ferns with their fairylike lacery;
Nodding of blooms with their blue, white, and yellow bells;
Over the pebbles brook-trebles like mellow bells;
Reed-note of robin and flute-note of vireo,
Jargon of jay and wren chatter so cheery-o;
Never a burden and never a care to see;
Everything blithesome and everything fair to see;
Every breath magical, every bough lyrical;
Just the unfolding of all the old miracle.

Greenery over and greenery under;
Out in the wood today, oh, such a wonder!

                              CLINTON SCOLLARD

*Here is a poem which uses words like colors from a
paint box. Your eyes see color and your ears hear
music. Can you find words that suggest movement?*

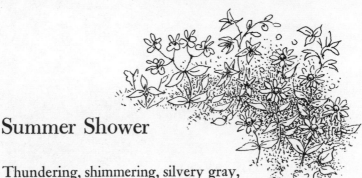

Summer Shower

Thundering, shimmering, silvery gray,
It's raining today,
Shining and slanting
Spears, such a shower as we've been wanting.

Freesia and fuchsia and mignonette
And violet
And golden glow
And blue delphinium, row on row,

And morning glory and hollyhock
And four-o'clock
And sweet alyssum
And bachelor button and cucumber blossom
And black-eyed susan and purple clover,
When the rain's over,
Will shake the shower
Out of each brimming, glistening flower.

And the sun will turn to a bright metal
Each bright petal;
When the rain's done
Each leaf and each petal will sparkle in the sun.

SELMA ROBINSON

Long ago, the poet Wordsworth accused the people of his day of too much competition for material things and not enough attention to the natural beauty provided by the Creator to delight and comfort the souls of men. "Getting and spending we lay waste our powers," he warned them. How does this poem make the same point? Do you remember who said, "I will lift up mine eyes unto the hills"?

The Weaving

The moon is weaving in the street
A tanglement for passing feet,

That must go always up and down
From the river to the town,

For men walk there who never see
The lovely gestures that a tree

Makes over them when they go by.
These men never see the sky.

Their hearts are heavy and they walk
With timid eyes. They never talk.

And so the moon is making there,
Out of her shining, beautiful hair,

Reflection of the branches so
That tired, awkward men may know

By looking on the ground they love
What excellent beauty moves above.

HAROLD LEWIS COOK

People who toil all day in factories or offices like to have something fresh and green to think of while they work. In large cities, some people never see a patch of green any larger than the little "Ellis Park" in this poem. Does it remind you of any place that you have seen? When you see a lovely place do you too "carry off a piece" in your mind?

Ellis Park

Little park that I pass through,
I carry off a piece of you
Every morning hurrying down
To my work-day in the town;
Carry you for country there
To make the city ways more fair.
I take your trees,
And your breeze,
Your greenness,
Your cleanness,
Some of your shade, some of your sky,
Some of your calm as I go by;
Your flowers to trim
The pavements grim;
Your space for room in the jostled street
And grass for carpet to my feet.

Your fountains take and sweet bird calls
To sing me from my office walls.

All that I can see
I carry off with me.
But you never miss my theft,
So much treasure you have left.
As I find you, fresh at morning,
So I find you, home returning—
Nothing lacking from your grace.
All your riches wait in place
For me to borrow
On the morrow.

Do you hear this praise of you,
Little park that I pass through?

HELEN HOYT

Fog has always interested the poets, probably because of the strange, mysterious changes it can make in our familiar world. Can you understand why the poet compares the world emerging from fog to God's work of creation?

Fog, the Magician

Wrapped in a cloak
Of grey mystery,
Fog, the magician,
Steals tip-toe out of the sea.
In seven-league boots
He skims across the sky,
Blowing out the sun,
Blotting out the blue.

On cobweb wires he slides to earth,
Glides through gardens surreptitiously,
And sponges every color out of flowers.
Churches, houses, trees,
He wipes like chalky outlines from a board.

Fog says—"Presto!"
And birds turn into nothing as they fly,
Men grow vague and vanish.
Fog claps his hands!
And motor-cars roll off into a void,
Dogs evaporate,
Cats dissolve to bodiless meows.

Noiselessly, peacefully,
The old world ends.
Nothing remains
But fog and me
And another world to be.
Slowly, dimly,
I seem to feel
A little of the wonder and the joy
That must have gladdened God in the beginning—
Creation before Him.

MELVILLE CANE

Read this poem very softly and see if you can make it sound like walking in velvet shoes. What are the "veils of white lace"?

Velvet Shoes

Let us walk in the white snow
   In a soundless space;
With footsteps quiet and slow,
   At a tranquil pace,
   Under veils of white lace.

I shall go shod in silk,
   And you in wool,
White as a white cow's milk,
   More beautiful
   Than the breast of a gull.

We shall walk through the still town
   In a windless peace;
We shall step upon white down,
   Upon silver fleece,
   Upon softer than these.

We shall walk in velvet shoes:
   Wherever we go
Silence will fall like dews
   On white silence below.
   We shall walk in the snow.

ELINOR WYLIE

City streets in late fall are usually bare and dingy, but the first snow can turn them into a fairy world. Words like diadem, spinster, *and* scintillating *should send you to your dictionary.*

To the City in the Snow

On brick and stone and trees all stark and bare
The snow comes softly, swiftly drifting down,
Transforming this prim spinster of a town
Into a sparkling princess passing fair.
With alabaster brow and frosty hair,
And icy jewels in her ermine gown,
She wears the glistening steeples for a crown,
And rears her crystal diadem in the air.

And then the moon sends down a silver beam,
The scintillating stars their sapphires show,
Amber and rose from friendly windows stream,
And multi-colored lights flash to and fro,
Tinting with fairy hue and dancing gleam
The too cold beauty of the fallen snow.

AGNES O'GARA RUGGERI

The winds are Nature's brooms, and March is the time for house cleaning. City streets and country meadows must be ready for the spring.

March Dreams

Winds of March, come sweeping through the long,
    brown valley.
Winds of March, ride flying through the dull, bare town.
Toss the crimsoned maples where the sodden leaves are lying,
Brush the yellowed mosses of the hills' gray gown.

Through the snow-banked meadow silent brooks are
    stealing.
Silver grasses shimmer where the bowed hedge sleeps.
Mist along the mountain slopes and white clouds wheeling;
Blurs of purple shadow that the brown wood keeps.

Winds of March, the lilies in the brick-bound gardens
Are lifting slender fingers through the sun-warmed sod.
And down the dingy parkway a dim ghost lingers,
A crumpled wraith of greenness like a twisted pagan god.

Winds of road and hilltop, breathe upon our dullness.
Winds of wood and ocean, sweep our sooty squares.
Some place in our dreaming there are rows of purple iris
Where a March wind frolics and a March sun flares.

ROSE HENDERSON

*You can tell that the man who wrote this poem had
often taken his turn at the wheel of a ship in all kinds
of weather. Note how the one-syllable words suggest
the sharp turns of the wheel. There are lovely musical
lines in the poem, too. Find lines that describe the sea
at dawn—at night—on a windy day.*

Sea-Fever

I must go down to the seas again, to the lonely sea
 and the sky,
And all I ask is a tall ship and a star to steer her by,
And the wheel's kick and the wind's song and the white
 sail's shaking,
And a grey mist on the sea's face and a grey dawn breaking.

I must go down to the seas again, for the call of the
 running tide
Is a wild call and a clear call that may not be denied;
And all I ask is a windy day with the white clouds flying,
And the flung spray and the blown spume, and the
 sea-gulls crying.

I must go down to the seas again to the vagrant gypsy life,
To the gull's way and the whale's way where the wind's like a
 whetted knife;
And all I ask is a merry yarn from a laughing fellow-rover,
And quiet sleep and a sweet dream when the long
 trick's over.

JOHN MASEFIELD

Usually it is the people who live in coastal towns and fishing villages who long to sail away, but sometimes the sea calls to people who have never even seen a towering, white-capped wave. Perhaps some far-off ancestor was a sailor, and through him the sea calls once again.

Voices

The restless sea is calling, and I would be away
To where the surf pounds up the beach to thunder in
      my ears,
To where the salt wind tastes like wine, and sailing
      vessels gay
Go out to strange sea-guarded ports and drift home gray
      with years.
From books and shells and scraps of tales these thoughts
      have come to me,
For I was born far inland who long to go to sea.

The midland has its voices, but they call to me in vain.
I care not for the whispering road nor drumming city street.
My heartbeats do not quicken to the thrush's joyous strain,
Nor to the sighing music of the wind upon the wheat.
The bees drone their contented song—but what is this
      to me?
For I was born far inland and long to hear the sea.

The sky is like the sea today and clouds like galleons ride—
I found a tiny river just beginning near the spring,
That called for me to follow and it would be my guide;
A boisterous echo in its tone, that yet was whispering,
Gave me a hint of ocean surge, and soon I know that we
Shall leave this inland country and make our way to sea.

JAMES S. HEARST

They say that a true sailor can never be content in harbor. When he knows that a ship is sailing, the sea's wild horses call him and even the joys of home cannot hold him—he must be off and away.

A Ship for Singapore

A ship is sailing for Singapore!
O heart be swift and latch the door!

My fire burns bright and the shadows fall
In yellow rhythms along the wall.
My love sleeps near and her dreams are deep,
Her lips a rose that has fallen asleep.
The fire burns bright and the candles glow,
And I must not go—I must not go!

There is no peace I can know to-night
Though my love sleeps near and the fire burns bright,
For stars will call from an Indian sky
And a gold moon haunt me blowing by.
The sea's wild horses will leap and fly,
Foam on their manes and wind in their eye!

O heart be swift and latch the door—
A ship is sailing for Singapore!

DANIEL WHITEHEAD HICKY

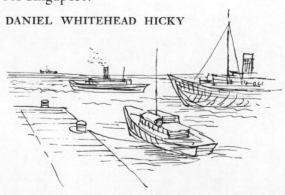

Find a picture of an old Roman quinquireme, *a ship with five banks of oars manned by galley slaves, or of a "stately Spanish galleon" with its carved prow and billowing sails. Compare them with the dingy little freighters that we still see in our modern harbors. What would you expect the cargoes of the different ships to be? The poet tells us a little about them. His poem makes us think of pirates and princesses and voyages of adventure.*

Cargoes

Quinquireme of Nineveh from distant Ophir
Rowing home to haven in sunny Palestine,
With a cargo of ivory,
And apes and peacocks,
Sandalwood, cedarwood, and sweet white wine.

Stately Spanish galleon coming from the Isthmus,
Dipping through the Tropics by the palm-green shores.
With a cargo of diamonds,
Emeralds, amethysts,
Topazes, and cinnamon, and gold moidores.

Dirty British coaster with a salt-caked smokestack,
Butting through the Channel in the mad March days,
With a cargo of Tyne coal,
Road-rails, pig-lead,
Firewood, iron-ware, and cheap tin trays.

JOHN MASEFIELD

An engineer or a pilot must have a tremendous sense of power and responsibility, remembering how much depends upon his skill and judgment. The pilot enjoys much of beauty, too, that is denied the engineer. The sea is often lonely, but the pilot sees the beauty and immensity.

Who Pilots Ships

Who pilots ships knows all a heart can know
Of beauty, and his eyes may close in death
And be content. There is no wind to blow
Whiter than foam-white wind and no wind's breath
Sweeter than tropic wind. There is no star
That throbs with cold white fire as North stars do,
No golden moon-path lovelier than the far
Path burning on the sea when dusk is blue.
There is no rain so swift as rain that flies
In bright battalions with a storm begun,
No song that shakes the heart like amber cries
Of gulls with wings turned yellow in the sun.
Who pilots ships, when life's last heartbeats stop,
Has drained the cup of beauty drop by drop.

DANIEL WHITEHEAD HICKY

Some people seem born to go forth to adventure, but others are like lightships. They must forever swing at anchor. Someone in the family—the mother, perhaps, or the eldest sister—stays at home, a haven for the others when they come back "beggared or riding deep." When does a ship ride deep?

The Lightship

Out with the tide, beneath the morning sun,
Along the highways of the wide bright sea
The ships go forth in beauty—even the smallest one
Goes forward eagerly!

Only the lightship, lonely, still, and proud,
Swings at her anchor, while a great undertow
Of passionate longing fills her, throbbing through keel and
    shroud,
For ports she may not know . . .

Then the blue dusk drops down, and from afar
The ships return. Beggared or riding deep,
For each a welcoming haven inside the harbor bar,
Furled canvas, quiet sleep.

But sleepless must the lightship lie, and lone
By the sharp reef—no dreams of curious lands,
Great burning unknown stars, bright birds, fantastic bone
Bleaching on island sands—

Never the voyage! Never the spreading sail!
Never the swift prow cutting through the foam
Of fabulous silver shorelines—after the fiercest gale,
Never the hope of home!

Steadfast and strong above the gathering chill
Her light burns on. How shall the passing bark
Surmise this desperate hunger? Lonely and proud and still
Are beacons in the dark!

JOSEPHINE JOHNSON

This description of the cranberry road reminds us of Cape Cod or some other section of the New England coast. Have you a favorite road or stretch of beach or some other scene that you are sure you will remember even when you are old?

Cranberry Road

I'd like to be walking the cranberry road,
  Where the sea shines blue through the bristling firs,
And the rocky pastures are over-grown
  With bayberry bushes and junipers;
Where orchards of bent old apple-trees
  Go trooping down to the pebbly shore,
And the clapboard houses are seaward turned,
  With larkspur clumps at every door;
Where there's plenty of time to say good-day
  When friendly eyes from a window peer—
Oh, I'd like to be back on the cranberry road;
  I wish I were there instead of here!

RACHEL FIELD

Dryads are beautiful fairy maidens who are supposed to live in trees. Here is the story of the one who is imprisoned in the birch tree.

The Spirit of the Birch

I am the dancer of the wood—
I shimmer in the solitude;
Men call me Birch Tree, yet I know
In other days it was not so.
I am a Dryad slim and white
Who danced too long one summer night,
And the Dawn found and prisoned me!
Captive I moan my liberty.
But let the wood wind flutes begin
Their elfin music, faint and thin,
I sway, I bend, retreat, advance,
And evermore—I dance! I dance!

ARTHUR KETCHUM

People used to believe that fairies sometimes stole chil-
dren from their cradles and left fairies instead. They
called such children "changelings." A changeling
would have a hard time doing dull, everyday tasks.
No wonder a changeling escaped sometimes to play
with trolls and leprechauns and the rest of the fairy
folk. Do you know any people who might perhaps be
changelings?

Changeling

She was a stately lady,
   And kept her in her place
Beside her lord and husband,
   In broideries and lace.

She stepped with pretty hauteur
   In pavan and quadrille.
(But once she skipped with urchins
   At moonrise on the hill.)

She crooned her plaintive ditties
   In verses prim and quaint;
Her lord and husband harkened
   And blest her for a saint.

She was a gracious lady,
   Serene to look upon.
(One night she plotted mischief
   With troll and leprechaun.)

She kept the castle strictly—
   The butlers and the maids;
Went all in white o' mornings,
   And wove her hair in braids.

She walked to church sedately
   And bent her down and prayed.
(But some one saw her follow
   Where gypsy folk had strayed.)

The day before last April
   She buttoned on her shoon
And off she went a-running,
   All in the afternoon.

And where-at-all she ended,
   Why, no one ever knew.
(But I could go and find her,
   Because I'm gypsy, too.)

                BARBARA YOUNG

Perhaps you think that this does not look like a poem
because the lines are so long and there is no rhyme, but
if you read it aloud you will find that the words have
a lovely sound. The Sidhe (pronounced "she") were
a fairy folk who lived in Ireland long and long ago.
This poem paints beautiful word pictures of their
warriors.

The Army of the Sidhe

Laegaire, son of the king of Connacht, was out one day with
the king his father near Loch na-n Ean, the Lake of Birds, and
the men of Connacht with them, and they saw a man coming
to them through the mist. Long golden-yellow hair he had,
and at his belt a gold-hilted sword, and in his hand two five-
barbed darts; a gold-rimmed shield on his back, a five-folded
crimson cloak about his shoulders, and it is what he said:

The most beautiful of plains is the Plain of the Two Mists;

it is not far from this; the men of its army in good order go out ahead of their beautiful king; they march among blue spears, white troops of fighters with curled hair.

They scatter the troops of their enemies, they destroy every country they make an attack on; they are beautiful in battle, a host with high looks, rushing, avenging.

It is no wonder they to have such strength; every one of them is the son of a king and a queen; manes of hair they have of the colour of gold.

Their bodies smooth and comely; their eyes blue and far-seeing; their teeth bright like crystal within their thin red lips.

White shields they have in their hands, with patterns on them of white silver; blue shining swords, red horns set with gold. They are good at killing men in battle; good at song-making; good at chess-playing.

The most beautiful of plains is the Plain of the Two Mists; it is not far from this place.

LADY GREGORY

It is just before you go to sleep, in that shadowy land
between asleep and awake, that you slowly climb the
Hills of Dream and meet the Host of Faerie.

From the
Hills of Dream

Across the silent stream
    Where the slumber-shadows go,
From the dim blue Hills of Dream
    I have heard the west wind blow.

Who hath seen that fragrant land,
    Who hath seen that unscanned west?
Only the listless hand
    And the unpulsing breast.

But when the west wind blows
    I see moon-lances gleam
Where the Host of Faerie flows
    Athwart the Hills of Dream.

And a strange song I have heard
    By a shadowy stream,
And the singing of a snow-white bird
    On the Hills of Dream.

FIONA MACLEOD

On the other side of the Hills of Dream is the Valley of White Poppies. Notice the lack of color in this poem. Every word contributes to the effect of silence and mystery.

The Valley of White Poppies

Between the grey pastures and the dark wood
A valley of white poppies is lit by the low moon:
   It is the grave of dreams, a holy rood.

   It is quiet there: no wind doth ever fall.
Long, long ago a wind sang once a heart-sweet rune.
   Now the white poppies grow, silent and tall.

   A white bird floats there like a drifting leaf:
It feeds upon faint sweet hopes and perishing dreams
   And the still breath of unremembering grief.

   And as a silent leaf the white bird passes,
Winnowing the dusk by dim forgetful streams.
   I am alone now among the silent grasses.

FIONA MACLEOD

Night Clouds

The white mares of the moon rush along the sky
Beating their golden hoofs upon the glass heavens;
The white mares of the moon are all standing on
  their hind legs
Pawing at the green porcelain doors of the
  remote heavens.

Fly, mares!
Strain your utmost,
Scatter the milky dust of stars,
Or the tiger sun will leap upon you and destroy you
With one lick of his vermilion tongue.

AMY LOWELL

This is a poem to read under a tree just when the light is fading. Watch for the Moon Child—it is easy to see her, but you must be very, very still to hear her "delicate, soft laughter."

A Tree at Dusk

With secrets in their eyes, the blue-winged Hours
Rustle through the meadow
Dropping shadow.

Yawning among red flowers,
The Moon Child with her golden hoop
And a pink star drifting after,
Leans to me where I droop.

I hear her delicate, soft laughter,
And through my hair her tiny fingers creep. . . .

I shall sleep.

WINIFRED WELLES

Listen to this colorful poem and try to think how the different cloths look. With what are they embroidered? Wouldn't they make a lovely gift for someone you love?

He Wishes for
the Cloths of Heaven

Had I the heavens' embroidered cloths,
Enwrought with golden and silver light,
The blue and the dim and the dark cloths
Of night and light and the half light,
I would spread the cloths under your feet:
But I, being poor, have only my dreams;
I have spread my dreams under your feet;
Tread softly because you tread on my dreams.

WILLIAM BUTLER YEATS

Hilaire Belloc has an odd, eerie sense of humor. Don't try to find out exactly what this poem means. Probably the poet didn't know.

The Moon's Funeral

The Moon is dead. I saw her die.
She in a drifting cloud was drest;
She lay along the uncertain west,
A dream to see.
And very low she spake to me:
"I go where none may understand,
I fade into the nameless land,
And there must lie perpetually."
And therefore I,
And therefore loudly, loudly I
And high
And very piteously make cry:
"The Moon is dead. I saw her die."

And will she never rise again?
The Holy Moon? Oh, never more!
Perhaps along the inhuman shore
Where pale ghosts are
Beyond the low lethean fen
She and some wide infernal star . . .
To us who loved her never more,
The Moon will never rise again.
Oh! never more in nightly sky
Her eye so high shall peep and pry
To see the great world rolling by.
For why?
The Moon is dead. I saw her die.

HILAIRE BELLOC

145

Have you ever played that you were a great king with a beautiful palace and trains of servants? What would you do if you were Lord of Tartary? Do you think you would ever get tired of it and wish you were a little boy or girl again?

Tartary

If I were Lord of Tartary,
   Myself and me alone,
My bed should be of ivory,
   Of beaten gold my throne;
And in my court should peacocks flaunt,
And in my forests tigers haunt,
And in my pools great fishes slant
   Their fins athwart the sun.

If I were Lord of Tartary,
   Trumpeters every day
To every meal should summon me,
   And in my courtyard bray;
And in the evening lamps would shine,
Yellow as honey, red as wine,
While harp, and flute, and mandoline,
   Made music sweet and gay.

If I were Lord of Tartary,
   I'd wear a robe of beads,
White, and gold, and green they'd be—
   And clustered thick as seeds;
And ere should wane the morning star,
I'd don my robe and scimitar,
And zebras seven should draw my car
   Through Tartary's dark glades.

Lord of the fruits of Tartary,
   Her rivers silver-pale!
Lord of the hills of Tartary,
   Glen, thicket, wood, and dale!
Her flashing stars, her scented breeze,
Her trembling lakes, like foamless seas,
Her bird-delighting citron-trees
   In every purple vale!

WALTER DE LA MARE

Have you ever, when you were washing dishes or helping Mother in other ways, wished that there were fairy godmothers today to make one's dreams come true? Perhaps you have thought, like this girl, that "after all and after all" there might be something pleasant just around the corner, even without a fairy godmother to help make it come true.

After All and After All

Dreaming of a prince
Cinderella sat among the ashes long ago;
Dreaming of a prince,
She scoured the pots and kettles till they shone; and so,
After all and after all,
Gaily at the castle ball
Cinderella met her prince long and long ago.

Dreaming of a prince
Sleeping Beauty lay in happy slumber, white and still;
Dreaming of a prince,
She waited for a hundred years and then his bugles shrill,
After all and after all,
Woke the castle, bower, and hall,
And he found her waiting for him long and long ago.

Dreaming of a prince
I polish bowl and teapot and the spoons, each one;
Dreaming of a prince,
I hang the new-washed clothes to wave a-drying in the sun;
After all and after all,
Great adventures may befall
Like to those that happened once long and long ago.

MARY CAROLYN DAVIES

This exquisite poem tells about a man who remembers in his heart the beautiful home of his youth and dreams always of going there to spend his declining years. When you read this poem aloud, notice how many times the soft "l" sound is repeated and what a peaceful, dreamy effect it gives. Where is the "Lake Isle" supposed to be?

The Lake Isle of Innisfree

I will arise and go now, and go to Innisfree,
And a small cabin build there, of clay and wattles made;
Nine bean rows will I have there, a hive for the honey bee,
And live alone in the bee-loud glade.

And I shall have some peace there, for peace comes
    dropping slow,
Dropping from the veils of the morning to where the
    cricket sings;
There midnight's all a glimmer, and noon a purple glow,
And evening full of the linnet's wings.

I will arise and go now, for always night and day
I hear lake water lapping with low sounds by the shore;
While I stand on the roadway, or on the pavement grey,
I hear it in the heart's deep core.

WILLIAM BUTLER YEATS

*In the days before the advent of air travel, the only
way to make the slow and dangerous journey across
the trackless desert was by caravan. Man's efforts to
find a way across the deserts of ignorance, cruelty, and
superstition have been something like caravans too,
pushing slowly on through the centuries. What progress have we made in transportation and commerce?
Why is our spiritual progress so slow?*

Caravans

Great, grey caravans moving in the night,
   Full of sullen mystery, laden down with heavy things;
Crowding through the darkness as they push on
     toward the light;
   Great, grey caravans, on great, grey wings.

Swift, silent caravans smashing through the night,
   Plunging over trackless wastes, wastes where trails
     can never meet,
Spraying noiseless gravel as they crowd on out of sight:
   Swift, silent caravans on swift, silent feet.

Soft, slow caravans swaying through the night,
   Tinkling bells and padded feet, and spices that the
     traders bought,
Easing through the moonlight, over sands dull white:
   Soft, slow caravans of soft, slow thought.

HAL BORLAND

Some people are domestic and like to stay at home; others suffer from wanderlust. The old English poet, Chaucer, said that in the spring especially we "long to go on pilgrimages." Do the brightly colored posters of the travel bureaus make you want to start forth, too? Where would you go first?

Travel

The railroad track is miles away,
  And the day is loud with voices speaking,
Yet there isn't a train goes by all day
  But I hear its whistle shrieking.

All night there isn't a train goes by,
  Though the night is still for sleep and dreaming,
But I see its cinders red on the sky,
  And hear its engine steaming.

My heart is warm with the friends I make,
  And better friends I'll not be knowing,
Yet there isn't a train I wouldn't take,
  No matter where it's going.

                    EDNA ST. VINCENT MILLAY

*This poem was written before man had begun to fill
the air with caravans of airplanes and even spaceships.
It is rich with an oriental beauty of sound and color
like that of the great Persian poet, Hafiz, who lived
long ago. Attar is essence of roses and myrrh is a spicy
gum like that which you sometimes find clinging to the
bark of trees. Find a map of the heavens, and some
clear night look for the Pleiades making a starry neck-
lace for the moon.*

A Caravan
from China Comes

A caravan from China comes;
   For miles it sweetens all the air
With fragrant silks and dreaming gums,
   Attar and myrrh—
A caravan from China comes.

O merchant, tell me what you bring,
   With music sweet of camel bells;
How long have you been travelling
   With these sweet smells?
O merchant, tell me what you bring.

A lovely lady is my freight,
   A lock escaped of her long hair,—
That is this perfume delicate
   That fills the air—
A lovely lady is my freight.

Her face is from another land,
   I think she is no mortal maid,—
Her beauty, like some ghostly hand,
   Makes me afraid;
Her face is from another land.

The little moon my cargo is,
   About her neck the Pleiades
Clasp hands and sing: Hafiz, 'tis this
   Perfumes the breeze—
The little moon my cargo is.

RICHARD LE GALLIENNE

You know what a palanquin is—an enclosed chair swinging on poles borne on the shoulders of the bearers. Palanquins used to be the chief means of transportation for rich and important people in India, China, and other oriental countries. The bearers often sang light-heartedly as they swung along the dusty road. Who do you suppose was in the palanquin in this poem? What was the occasion? Why did the bearers find the lady so light a burden?

Palanquin Bearers

Lightly, O lightly, we bear her along,
She sways like a flower in the wind of our song;
She skims like a bird on the foam of a stream,
She floats like a laugh from the lips of a dream.
Gaily, O gaily, we glide and we sing,
We bear her along like a pearl on a string.

Softly, O softly, we bear her along,
She hangs like a star in the dew of our song;
She springs like a beam on the brow of the tide,
She falls like a tear from the eyes of a bride;
Lightly, O lightly, we glide and we sing,
We bear her along like a pearl on a string.

SAROJINI NAIDU

The Japanese people are gifted with the ability to express a great deal in a very few words or with just a few strokes of the brush. The tanka is one of their popular forms of verse, most of which have only five lines and a definite number of syllables. They are, as a rule, untitled and usually recall an incident, record an observation or make some comment on human life and thought. Emperor Hirohito, who is very skillful at writing verse, composed the following tanka. What do you think made the Emperor recall that particular day at Shino Point? What is the key word?

A Memory

As I
Was visiting
The Shino Point in Kii
Clouds were drifting far
Over the Sea.

EMPEROR HIROHITO OF JAPAN

An Indian bazaar is one of the most colorful scenes in the world. In this poem we experience all the sights, sounds, and odors of the busy market.

In the Bazaars of Hyderabad

What do you sell, O ye merchants?
Richly your wares are displayed.
Turbans of crimson and silver,
Tunics of purple brocade,
Mirrors with panels of amber,
Daggers with handles of jade.

What do you weigh, O ye vendors?
Saffron and lentil and rice.
What do you grind, O ye maidens?
Sandalwood, henna, and spice.
What do you call, O ye pedlars?
Chessmen and ivory dice.

What do you make, O ye goldsmiths?
Wristlet and anklet and ring,
Bells for the feet of blue pigeons,
Frail as a dragon-fly's wing,
Girdles of gold for the dancers,
Scabbards of gold for the king.

What do you cry, O ye fruitmen?
Citron, pomegranate, and plum.
What do you play, O musicians?
Cithar, sarangi, and drum.
What do you chant, O magicians?
Spells for æons to come.

What do you weave, O ye flower-girls
With tassels of azure and red?
Crowns for the brow of a bridegroom,
Chaplets to garland his bed,
Sheets of white blossoms new-gathered
To perfume the sleep of the dead.

SAROJINI NAIDU

It is always interesting to note how much human beings are alike no matter in what country or what period of time they live. The experience of turning homeward nearly always arouses the same emotions in the human heart, as in the case of this man of ancient China who finds comfort in the familiar sights of home. Chinese letters are drawn with a brush.

Sailing Homeward

Cliffs that rise a thousand feet
Without a break,
Lake that stretches a hundred miles
Without a wave,
Sands that are white through all the year
Without a stain,
Pine-tree woods, winter and summer
Evergreen,
Streams that forever flow and flow
Without a pause,
Trees that for twenty thousand years
Your vows have kept,
You have suddenly healed the pain of a traveler's heart,
And moved his brush to write a new song.

CHAN FANG-SHENG
Arthur Waley, Translator

This poem is really perfect, with its strong rhythmic beat. Read it in a low even chant, keeping the beat of the drums in mind. In the third and fourth lines each of the words "low" and "slow" has four counts.

African Dance

The low beating of the tom-toms,
The slow beating of the tom-toms,
    Low . . . slow
    Slow . . . low—
Stirs your blood.

        Dance!
A night-veiled girl
    Whirls softly into a
    Circle of light.
Whirls softly . . . slowly,
Like a wisp of smoke around the fire—
    And the tom-toms beat,
    And the tom-toms beat,
And the low beating of the tom-toms
    Stirs your blood.

                LANGSTON HUGHES

*Sherwood Forest in far-away England is the place
where lived bold Robin Hood. If you should walk in
Sherwood, do you think you could shut your eyes
and hear the fairy horns—see the ghosts of Robin and
his merry men as the poet did?*

A Song of Sherwood

Sherwood in the twilight, is Robin Hood awake?
Grey and ghostly shadows are gliding through the brake,
Shadows of the dappled deer, dreaming of the morn,
Dreaming of a shadowy man that winds a shadowy horn.

Robin Hood is here again; all his merry thieves
Hear a ghostly bugle-note shivering through the leaves,
Calling as he used to call, faint and far away,
In Sherwood, in Sherwood, about the break of day.

Merry, merry England has kissed the lips of June;
All the wings of fairyland were here beneath the moon,
Like a flight of rose-leaves fluttering in a mist
Of opal and ruby and pearl and amethyst.

Merry, merry England is waking as of old,
With eyes of blither hazel and hair of brighter gold;
For Robin Hood is here again beneath the bursting spray
In Sherwood, in Sherwood, about the break of day.

Love is in the greenwood building him a house
Of wild rose and hawthorn and honeysuckle boughs;
Love is in the greenwood, dawn is in the skies,
And Marian is waiting with a glory in her eyes.

Hark! The dazzled laverock climbs the golden steep!
Marian is waiting; is Robin Hood asleep?
Round the fairy grass-rings frolic elf and fay,
In Sherwood, in Sherwood, about the break of day.

Oberon, Oberon, rake away the gold,
Rake away the red leaves, roll away the mould,
Rake away the gold leaves, roll away the red,
And wake Will Scarlett from his leafy forest bed.

Friar Tuck and Little John are riding down together
With quarter-staff and drinking-can and grey goose feather.
The dead are coming back again, the years are rolled away
In Sherwood, in Sherwood, about the break of day.

Softly over Sherwood the south wind blows.
All the heart of England hid in every rose
Hears across the greenwood the sunny whisper leap,
Sherwood in the red dawn, is Robin Hood asleep?

Hark, the voice of England wakes him as of old
And, shattering the silence with a cry of brighter gold,
Bugles in the greenwood echo from the steep,
Sherwood in the red dawn, is Robin Hood asleep?

Where the deer are gliding down the shadowy glen
All across the glades of fern he calls his merry men—
Doublets of the Lincoln green glancing through the May
In Sherwood, in Sherwood, about the break of day—

Calls them and they answer; from aisles of oak and ash
Rings the *Follow! Follow!* and the boughs begin to crash,
The ferns begin to flutter and the flowers begin to fly,
And through the crimson dawning the robber band goes by.

Robin! Robin! Robin! All his merry thieves
Answer as the bugle-note shivers through the leaves,
Calling as he used to call, faint and far away,
In Sherwood, in Sherwood, about the break of day.

ALFRED NOYES

Almost every tourist who visits England goes to Strat-
ford to pay tribute to William Shakespeare who wrote
the greatest plays in our language. They rarely leave
without walking across to the cottage of Anne Hath-
away, the girl Shakespeare married. The minds of
the great creative thinkers such as poets, philosophers,
and dramatists are not constantly filled with high and
noble thoughts. What did Shakespeare occasionally
have on his mind?

The Path to Shottery

Over the fields to Shottery, fresh with a wet-green scent,
The path leads through the haws and wheat, the path the Poet
    went.

A skylark staying up too late is fearful to go home,
And blades of grass begin to stir where little beetles roam.

What was he musing on the path to twilit Shottery?
What captive song was in his heart that struggled to be free?

Did he know his little candle would forever throw its beams,
Did he think the world would tremble at the beauty
    of his dreams?

Or was the Poet wondering, as he chewed a blade of grass,
If he should walk that night with Anne or choose some
    Stratford lass?

                CORNELIA OTIS SKINNER

A tarantella is a kind of lilting dance that delights the people of Spain and Italy. You can feel the swing and the beat of the tarantella in this poem, which recalls happy, carefree days that will never come again.

Tarantella

Do you remember an Inn, Miranda?
Do you remember an Inn?
And the tedding and the spreading
Of the straw for a bedding,
And the fleas that tease in the High Pyrenees,
And the wine that tasted of the tar?
And the cheers and the jeers of the young muleteers
(Under the vine of the dark verandah)—
Do you remember an Inn, Miranda?
Do you remember an Inn?
And the cheers and the jeers of the young muleteers
Who hadn't got a penny
And who weren't paying any,
And the hammer at the doors and the din?

And the Hip!   Hop!   Hap!
Of the clap
Of the hands to the twirl and the swirl
Of the girl gone chancing,
Glancing,
Dancing,
Backing and advancing,
Snapping of the clapper to the spin
Out and in—
And the ting, tong, tang of the Guitar!
Do you remember an Inn, Miranda?
Do you remember an Inn?

Never more, Miranda;
Never more.
Only the high peaks hoar;
And Aragon torrent at the door.
No sound
In the walls of the Halls where falls
The tread
Of the feet of the dead to the ground.
No sound:
But the boom
Of the far Waterfall like Doom.

HILAIRE BELLOC

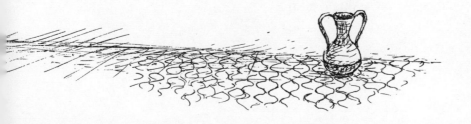

Do you ever try to imagine what stories lie behind the objects bought and sold so casually at auctions and antique shops? Perhaps you could learn some of those stories from the older generations in your own family.

Antique Shop

I knew an old lady
A long time ago
Who rocked while she told me
The things I should know.

She lies in her grave now
And I am a man
But here is her rocker
And here is her fan.

Her fan and her rocker
Are all that remain
But I can still see her
Rock-rocking
Talk-talking,
Rock-rocking,
Again.

    CARL CARMER

There is a section in the city of New Orleans known as "French Town." Visitors are always charmed by the quaint old-world flavor. The Cathedral of St. Louis is old, gray and haunted by memories. This poem describes its appearance in early evening when the Angelus bell rings and all the people stop to say their evening prayers.

The Cathedral of St. Louis

I know I shall remember
When it is time to die
Those towers, that cross, at evening
Against the mellow sky.

    And life shall leave me lightly
(I shall not know nor care)
Like a chime of bell notes drifting
Across the shadowed square.

CARL CARMER

We all love our country, but we never realize how much until we leave it for a time. How can you tell that the poet is talking especially about travelers and tourists on relatively short trips? What would be the feelings of a diplomat, a newspaper correspondent, the business manager of a foreign branch or others who have to remain abroad for long periods? What do soldiers appreciate most after a tour of foreign duty? Read the last line of the next-to-last stanza. What could we do to make our land even better?

America for Me

'Tis fine to see the Old World, and travel up and down
Among the famous palaces and cities of renown,
To admire the crumbly castles and the statues of the kings,—
But now I think I've had enough of antiquated things.

So it's home again, and home again, America for me!
My heart is turning home again, and there I long to be,
In the land of youth and freedom beyond the ocean bars,
Where the air is full of sunlight and the flag is full of stars.

Oh, London is a man's town, there's power in the air;
And Paris is a woman's town, with flowers in her hair;
And it's sweet to dream in Venice, and it's great
  to study Rome;
But when it comes to living there is no place like home.

I like the German fir-woods, in green battalions drilled;
I like the gardens of Versailles with flashing fountains filled;

But, oh, to take your hand, my dear, and ramble for a day
In the friendly western woodland where Nature has her way!

I know that Europe's wonderful, yet something
　　seems to lack:
The Past is too much with her, and the people looking back.
But the glory of the Present is to make the Future free,—
We love our land for what she is and what she is to be.

Oh, it's home again, and home again, America for me!
I want a ship that's westward bound to plough
　　the rolling sea,
To the blessed Land of Room Enough beyond
　　the ocean bars,
Where the air is full of sunlight and the flag is full of stars.

HENRY VAN DYKE

Some people think that there is no such place as heaven because we have never seen it. The writer of this poem considers that a foolish argument because there are so many other things in which we believe although we have not seen them. She mentions several. How many can you add?

I Never Saw a Moor

I never saw a moor,
I never saw the sea;
Yet know I how the heather looks,
And what a wave must be.

I never spoke with God,
Nor visited in heaven;
Yet certain am I of the spot
As if the chart were given.

EMILY DICKINSON

Many people refuse to believe in God because they cannot see Him. The poet wonders here why we accept so readily the miracles of science, which after all are made only by man, and even doubt for an instant that God can hear our prayers.

Proof

If radio's slim fingers
   Can pluck a melody
From night and toss it over
   A continent or sea;
If songs, like crimson roses,
   Are culled from thin, blue air,
Why should mortals wonder
   If God can hear their prayer?

ETHEL ROMIG FULLER

A Chant Out of Doors

God of grave nights,
God of brave mornings,
God of silent noon,
Hear my salutation!

   For where the rapids rage white and scornful,
   I have passed safely, filled with wonder;
   Where the sweet pools dream under willows,
   I have been swimming, filled with life.

God of round hills,
God of green valleys,
God of clear springs,
Hear my salutation!

   For where the moose feeds, I have eaten berries,
   Where the moose drinks, I have drunk deep.
   When the storms crash through broken heavens—
   And under clear skies—I have known joy.

God of great trees,
God of wild grasses,
God of little flowers,
Hear my salutation!

For where the deer crops and the beaver plunges,
Near the river I have pitched my tent;
Where the pines cast aromatic needles
On a still floor, I have known peace.

God of grave nights,
God of brave mornings,
God of silent noon,
Hear my salutation.

MARGUERITE WILKINSON

*Nearly every child knows a little prayer to say before
and after meals, but who ever heard of a grace for
light? The children in this far-away olden-times Irish
household behaved much as you do when you are getting ready for bed. What is meant by She and Herself
and Himself? The rush-dip was a candle cut from the
inner pith of long green rushes and dipped in oil or
grease. Why have we, in these days, more reason to
say the grace for light than the family who lived in the
wee house "up Brabla' way"?*

Grace for Light

When we were little childer we had a quare wee house,
   Away up in the heather by the head o' Brabla' Burn;
The hares we'd see them scootin', an' we'd hear the crowin'
     grouse,
    An' when we'd all be in at night ye'd not get
     room to turn.

The youngest two She'd put to bed, their faces to the wall,
   An' the lave of us could sit aroun', just anywhere
    we might;
Herself 'ud take the rush-dip an' light it for us all,
    An' *"God be thanked!"* She would say,—*"now we
    have a light."*

Then we be to quet the laughin' an' pushin' on the floor,
   An' think on One who called us to come and be forgiven;
Himself 'ud put his pipe down, an' say the good word more,
   "May the Lamb o' God lead us all to the Light o' Heaven!"

There's a wheen things that used to be an' now has had
      their day,
   The nine Glens of Antrim can show ye many a sight;
But not the quare wee house where we lived up Brabla' way,
   Nor a child in all the nine Glens that knows the grace
      for light.

                                        MOIRA O'NEILL

The old Irish blessing for light is no longer in use, but in many Jewish homes the Sabbath candles are lighted each Friday evening and this beautiful prayer-poem is said.

Blessing for Light

Blessed Art Thou,
O Lord our God,
King of the Universe,
Who has sanctified us
By Thy commandments
And commanded us
To kindle the Sabbath light.

*The Jewish people have an annual eight-day festival
of light called Hanukkah. At this time they use a can-
delabrum called a Menorah which has a candle for
each of the days and a special candle used to light the
others. Hanukkah commemorates Judah the Maccabee
who, after leading a revolt against the Syrian King
Antiochus, relit the sacred lamp in the great Temple.*

Eight Are the Lights

Eight are the lights
   of Hanukkah
We light for a week
   And a day.
We kindle the lights,
   And bless the Lord,
And sing a song,
   And pray.

      Eight are the lights
         of Hanukkah
      For *justice* and *mercy*
         and *love*,
      For *charity*, *courage*
         and *honor* and *peace*,
      And *faith* in Heaven
         above.

Eight are the lights
   of Hanukkah
To keep ever bright
   Memories
Of the valiant soul
   And the fighting heart
And the hope of the
   Maccabees!

ILO ORLEANS

Because the light of faith has remained in the hearts of the Jewish people even as the sacred lamp was always kept lighted in the great Temple in Jerusalem, this poem is called "A Song of Always."

A Song of Always

The Temple is clean
   The lamp burns bright;
Judah the leader,
   Has started the light.

The sun shines by day,
   And dark is the night;
But always and always
   The lamp burns bright.

EFRAIM ROSENZWEIG

Here are some things for which we should remember
to give thanks every day. Can you think of others?
How can we grow nearer the sky?

A Little Song of Life

Glad that I live am I;
That the sky is blue;
Glad for the country lanes,
And the fall of dew.

After the sun the rain,
After the rain the sun;
This is the way of life,
Till the work be done.

All that we need to do,
Be we low or high,
Is to see that we grow
Nearer the sky.

LIZETTE WOODWORTH REESE

Here is a poem that makes us feel a little differently toward the people who serve us, whether in big stores or little shops. Those described in this poem would have been found in an old-fashioned English village. An iron-monger would keep a hardware shop. The word "without" in the last stanza means beyond. What hopes and dreams might lie beyond the blue horizons of some of the clerks who wait on you?

Shops

I like the people who keep shops,
Busy and cheerful folk with friendly faces.
They handle only lovely things—bulbs, seed and flowers,
China and glass and gay-backed magazines,
Velvet and satin, foreign silks and laces.

One keeps a stall that's good to see,
Of nuts and fruit the morning sunlight dapples,
With dewy green things fresh from country gardens,
Tomatoes, bloomy plums and figs in baskets,
Melons and pears, and red or russet apples.

The ironmonger charms me, too,
With wholesome things of house and ground for selling,
Rakes, hoes and spades, tinware and tacks and hammers,

And shining lamps that wait for kindling fingers,
A pleasant place for converse, good, clean-smelling.

To serve us seems their only aim,
Asking our wishes, quick to crave our pardon,
And yet I know in each of these shop people
There dwells a soul withdrawn from us, elusive,
The shop can never know—a secret garden.

How can we guess who see them so,
Behind their counters, writing down our orders,
The hidden glades of thought, the fair surprises
That lie without our reach, the blue horizons
Stretching for them beyond their peaceful borders?

WINIFRED M. LETTS

*Sometimes children (and their elders, too) are very
cruel to people who are old and poor and a little queer.
They follow them along the street and make up rhymes
to tease them. What kind of person do you think the
Vinegar Man might have been when he was young?
Why did he tear the valentine? Was Ellen to blame?
How does the poem suggest that his life really ended
there? Is there anything that you could do to make
some lonely person happy?*

The Vinegar Man

The crazy old Vinegar Man is dead! He never had missed a
　　day before!
Somebody went to his tumble-down shed by the Haunted
　　House and forced the door.
There in the litter of his pungent pans, the murky mess of his
　　mixing place—
Deep, sticky spiders and empty cans—with the same old
　　frown on his sour old face.

"Vinegar—Vinegar—Vinegar Man!
Face—us—and—chase—us—and—catch—if—you—can!
Pepper for a tongue! Pickle for a nose!
Stick a pin in him and vinegar flows!
Glare—at—us—swear—at—us—catch—if—you—can!
Ketchup—and—chow—chow—and—Vinegar—Man!"

Nothing but recipes and worthless junk; greasy old records of
　　paid and due;

But down in the depths of a battered trunk, a queer, quaint
    valentine torn in two—
Red hearts and arrows and silver lace, and a prim, dim, lady-
    like script that said—
(Oh, Vinegar Man, with the sour old face!)—"With dearest
    love, from Ellen to Ned!"

"Steel—us—and—peel—us—and—drown—us—in—brine!
He pickles his heart in"—*a valentine!*
"Vinegar for blood! Pepper for his tongue!
Stick a pin in him and—" *once he was young!*
"Glare—at—us—swear—at—us—catch—if—you—can!"—
"With dearest love"—*to the Vinegar Man!*

Dingy little books of profit and loss (died about Saturday, so
    they say),
And a queer, quaint valentine torn across . . . torn, but it
    never was thrown away!
"With dearest love from Ellen to Ned"—"Old Pepper
    Tongue! Pickles his heart in brine!"
The Vinegar Man is a long time dead: he died when he tore
    his valentine.

RUTH COMFORT MITCHELL

If you were old and poor and had to wander about the roads begging your way, with no place to lay your head, what would you want most of all? There are many such unfortunate old women all over the world, particularly in those countries where so many families are uprooted and displaced by war. The one who speaks in this poem lived in Ireland long ago. Which stanza makes you feel cold and lonesome? Which stanza makes a cozy, comfortable picture? Can you pick out some of the words which help to make these pictures?

An Old Woman
of the Roads

O to have a little house!
To own the hearth and stool and all!
The heaped up sods upon the fire,
The pile of turf against the wall!

To have a clock with weights and chains
And pendulum swinging up and down!
A dresser filled with shining delph,
Speckled and white and blue and brown!

I could be busy all the day
Clearing and sweeping hearth and floor,
And fixing on their shelf again
My white and blue and speckled store!

I could be quiet there at night
Beside the fire and by myself,
Sure of a bed and loth to leave
The ticking clock and the shining delph!

Och! but I'm weary of mist and dark,
And roads where there's never a house nor bush,
And tired I am of bog and road
And the crying wind and the lonesome hush!

And I am praying to God on high,
And I am praying Him night and day,
For a little house—a house of my own—
Out of the wind's and the rain's way.

PADRAIC COLUM

Do you know any "lone-dog" people who are cross and ill-tempered, refuse to play with others and seem to prefer to sulk by themselves? Such persons are often very lonely and unhappy. They would like to be friendly, but they don't know how. Read the first two lines in the last stanza again. Don't they sound a little wistful?

Lone Dog

I'm a lean dog, a keen dog, a wild dog, and lone;
I'm a rough dog, a tough dog, hunting on my own;
I'm a bad dog, a mad dog, teasing silly sheep;
I love to sit and bay the moon, to keep fat souls from sleep.

I'll never be a lap dog, licking dirty feet,
A sleek dog, a meek dog, cringing for my meat,
Not for me the fireside, the well-filled plate,
But shut door, and sharp stone, and cuff and kick and hate.

Not for me the other dogs, running by my side,
Some have run a short while, but none of them would bide.
O mine is still the lone trail, the hard trail, the best,
Wide wind, and wild stars, and hunger of the quest!

IRENE RUTHERFORD MCLEOD

Some people might be disappointed at receiving a legacy of "a little sloping acre" instead of jewels or money. Which would you rather have?

Legacy

I had a rich old great-aunt
Who left me, when she died,
A little sloping acre
And not a thing beside.

Nothing else she left me
But a clump of sweet phlox
And an old silver aspen
And some hollyhocks.

A humming-bird disputed
My heritage with me,
And so did a robin
And a gold-backed bee.

A cricket owned a hummock,
He couldn't say how;
Two wrens held a mortgage
On one aspen bough.

A toad claimed a corner
(He said it was a lease).
We learned to live together
In a sort of cheery peace.

Never such an acre
To mortal was given!
My good old great-aunt,
May she rest in heaven!

NANCY BYRD TURNER

Do you think the author of this poem is describing one of her neighbors, or herself as she imagines her neighbors regard her? Note that the title uses the preposition "by." What difference would it make if you substituted "of"? Is the tone of the poem really critical or is it rather sympathetic? What are some of the lines in the description that would fit that of a poet? Would you like to live next door?

Portrait by a Neighbor

Before she has her floor swept
   Or her dishes done,
Any day you'll find her
   A-sunning in the sun!

It's long after midnight
   Her key's in the lock,
And you never see her chimney smoke
   Till past ten o'clock!

She digs in her garden
   With a shovel and a spoon,
She weeds her lazy lettuce
   By the light of the moon,

She walks up the walk
   Like a woman in a dream,
She forgets she borrowed butter
   And pays you back cream!

Her lawn looks like a meadow,
   And if she mows the place
She leaves the clover standing
   And the Queen Anne's lace!

EDNA ST. VINCENT MILLAY

Not all the knowledge in the world is found in books. Many a "half-wit" knows secrets that the rest of us have never even guessed. Keep the proper pronunciation of "breeches" ("britches") here, even though it does not rhyme exactly with "reaches."

Village Portrait

He was the half-wit of that prairie town,
The butt of every loafer's jest. His shack
Drowsed in a heap south of the railroad track
Near Perkins' slough. When winter settled down
And blizzards swept across the prairie reaches,
He'd huddle there and feed his fire. The door
Leaked cold. He'd watch the frost crawl on the floor
And slap his numb arms down against his breeches.

He was the half-wit. But we boys soon found
No other knew so well where red haws grew,
Or where the black-cased walnuts stained the ground,
And when the yellow sunfish bit. He knew
The thrush's song in spring, and understood
How to trail wild things through a snowy wood.

THOMAS W. DUNCAN

The story of Amelia Earhart is one of the highlights of American aviation. If you don't know it, be sure to look it up. This poem is particularly significant because of her tragic fate. Perhaps she would not have called it tragic. She made her choice and "dared the soul's dominion." No doubt she would have said that the price was not too high.

Courage

Courage is the price that life exacts for granting peace.
The soul that knows it not, knows no release
From little things;

Knows not the livid loneliness of fear
Nor mountain heights, where bitter joy can hear
The sound of wings.

How can life grant us boon of living, compensate
For dull gray ugliness and pregnant hate
Unless we dare

The soul's dominion? Each time we make a choice, we pay
With courage to behold resistless day
And count it fair.

AMELIA EARHART

This poem was written before the space age, but it still describes the grandeur and excitement of man's never-ending search to learn the secrets of the universe.

To an Aviator

You who have grown so intimate with stars
And know their silver dripping from your wings,
Swept with the breaking day across the sky,
Known kinship with each meteor that swings—
You who have touched the rainbow's fragile gold,
Carved lyric ways through dawn and dusk and rain
And soared to heights our hearts have only dreamed—
How can you walk earth's common ways again?

DANIEL WHITEHEAD HICKY

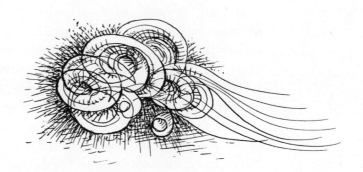

If you have ever seen a polo game, even if only on television, you will realize that the poet has caught here all the sound, movement and intense excitement of a game that is a test of skill and endurance for horse as well as man.

Polo Player

Swift as an arrow in the wind he goes
Across the stretching velvet of the grass;
Like sudden music now he leaps and flows
In quickening rhythms as the hoofbeats pass.
They poise in space a fleeting moment, curve
Close to the ground again; now higher, higher,
They take the wind again; they leap, they swerve
With all the maddening passion of a fire.
The mallets whiz along the wind, they click
Staccato-like, again they whirr and rise;
Far quicker than the swiftest wind is quick
He sweeps across the field; his squinting eyes
Fast on the ball, he sees it leap and roll . . .
His blood shouts in his veins, the goal, the goal!

DANIEL WHITEHEAD HICKY

This haunting little poem should help you to remember never to make fun of anyone because he is different from you in appearance, speech, dress or in any other way.

Incident

Once riding in Old Baltimore,
Heart filled, head filled with glee,
I saw a Baltimorean
Staring straight at me.

Now I was eight and very small,
And he was no whit bigger
And so I smiled, but he
Stuck out his tongue and called me nigger.

I saw the whole of Baltimore
From May until November.
Of all the things that happened there—
That's all that I remember.

COUNTEE CULLEN

Joan of Arc, or Jeanne d'Arc as she is called in France, was a holy maid. Dressed in shining armor and riding a white charger, she led the French armies in a long ago war. During the Second World War, the French people used to think that her spirit came back and rode up and down the land, cheering and encouraging the soldiers.

The Good Joan

Along the thousand roads of France,
Now there, now here, swift as a glance,
A cloud, a mist blown down the sky,
Good Joan of Arc goes riding by.

In Domremy at candlelight,
The orchards blowing rose and white
About the shadowy houses lie;
And Joan of Arc goes riding by.

On Avignon there falls a hush,
Brief as the singing of a thrush
Across old gardens April-high;
And Joan of Arc goes riding by.

The women bring the apples in,
Round Arles when the long gusts begin,
Then sit them down to sob and cry;
And Joan of Arc goes riding by.

Dim fall the hoofs down old Calais;
In Tours a flash of silver-gray,
Like flaw of rain in a clear sky;
And Joan of Arc goes riding by.

Who saith that ancient France shall fail,
A rotting leaf driv'n down the gale?
Then her sons know not how to die;
Then good God dwells no more on high!

Tours, Arles, and Domremy reply!
For Joan of Arc goes riding by.

LIZETTE   WOODWORTH   REESE

*The soldiers who fought in the First World War did
so in the hope that they could make the world so safe
that there would be no more wars. Was their hope
realized? What wars have we fought since then? This
poem was found in the pocket of the soldier who wrote
it after he had died in battle. He knew that many of his
comrades would surely die, and he begged all those
who followed to hold the torch of freedom high and
fight for the dignity and equality of all men. There
were so many poppies in France and Flanders that the
flower became a symbol and eventually the emblem of
the American Legion.*

In Flanders Fields

In Flanders fields the poppies blow
Between the crosses, row on row,
    That mark our place; and in the sky
    The larks, still bravely singing, fly
Scarce heard amid the guns below.

We are the dead. Short days ago
We lived, felt dawn, saw sunset glow,
    Loved and were loved, and now we lie
      In Flanders fields.

Take up our quarrel with the foe:
To you from failing hands we throw
    The torch; be yours to hold it high.
    If ye break faith with us who die
We shall not sleep, though poppies grow
      In Flanders fields.

JOHN MCCRAE

Most human beings start out in life with dreams of suc-
cess and happiness. Some achieve all their goals appar-
ently almost without trying. Others, because of barriers
of race, creed, color or physical condition, are obliged
to lay their dreams away and face an uncertain future.
Have the successful of this world any obligation to
help their less fortunate brothers? What are some of
the best ways to help?

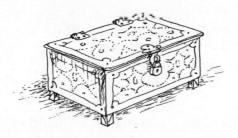

I Have Wrapped My
Dreams in a Silken Cloth

I have wrapped my dreams in a silken cloth
And laid them away in a box of gold,
Where long may cling the lips of the moth;
I have wrapped my dreams in a silken cloth.
I hide no hate; I am not even wroth
Who found life's breath so keen and cold.
I have wrapped my dreams in a silken cloth
And laid them away in a box of gold.

COUNTEE CULLEN

Look at a picture of Lincoln and think a little about his character. Then consider what a remarkable word-picture this poem paints. What was the "mad stray bolt from the zenith" that struck down our great President?

Lincoln

Like a gaunt, scraggly pine
Which lifts its head above the mournful sandhills;
And patiently, through dull years of bitter silence,
Untended and uncared for, starts to grow.

Ungainly, laboring, huge,
The wind of the north has twisted and gnarled its branches;
Yet in the heat of mid-summer days, when thunder clouds
    ring the horizon,
A nation of men shall rest beneath its shade.

And it shall protect them all,
Hold everyone safe there, watching aloof in silence;
Until at last, one mad stray bolt from the zenith
Shall strike it in an instant down to earth.

JOHN GOULD FLETCHER

Barter means "trade" or "exchange." Do you suppose that old Scrooge in "The Christmas Carol" could have exchanged one of his gold pieces for any of the lovely things this poem tells us about? There are things to see and hear and feel and smell, but the joy they bring cannot be bought for money. Can you think of any bits of "loveliness" that the poet has left out?

Barter

Life has loveliness to sell,
   All beautiful and splendid things,
Blue waves whitened on a cliff,
   Soaring fire that sways and sings,
And children's faces looking up
Holding wonder like a cup.

Life has loveliness to sell,
   Music like a curve of gold,
Scent of pine trees in the rain,
   Eyes that love you, arms that hold,
And for your spirit's still delight,
Holy thoughts that star the night.

Spend all you have for loveliness,
   Buy it and never count the cost;
For one white singing hour of peace
   Count many a year of strife well lost,
And for a breath of ecstasy
Give all you have been, or could be.

SARA TEASDALE

Read "Moon Folly," the "Song of Conn the Fool," on page 24. How are Aengus and Conn alike? Why would Aengus like Conn's moon tree?

The Song
of Wandering Aengus

I went out to the hazel wood,
Because a fire was in my head,
And cut and peeled a hazel wand,
And hooked a berry to a thread;
And when white moths were on the wing,
And moth-like stars were flickering out,
I dropped the berry in a stream
And caught a little silver trout.

When I had laid it on the floor
I went to blow the fire a-flame,
But something rustled on the floor,
And some one called me by my name;
It had become a glimmering girl
With apple blossom in her hair
Who called me by my name and ran
And faded through the brightening air.

Though I am old with wandering
Through hollow lands and hilly lands,
I will find out where she has gone,
And kiss her lips and take her hands;
And walk among long dappled grass,
And pluck till time and times are done,
The silver apples of the moon,
The golden apples of the sun.

WILLIAM BUTLER YEATS

Even when a whole day seems spoiled because of some-thing we are sorry about, some simple touch of natural beauty will often set things right again.

Dust of Snow

The way a crow
   Shook down on me
The dust of snow
   From a hemlock tree

Has given my heart
   A change of mood
And saved some part
   Of a day I had rued.

ROBERT FROST

The person who speaks in this poem is one of those who suffer defeat and loneliness because they are physically unattractive or think they are, and the world passes them by in favor of outward beauty. Have you ever noticed that some of the least attractive people, by worldly standards, are the kindest, the most helpful, the most sympathetic, and often among the most intelligent? It might pay to take a second look and find out what their souls are like. And, by the way, what are you giving your soul to wear?

Souls

My Soul goes clad in gorgeous things,
Scarlet and gold and blue,
And at her shoulder sudden wings
Like long flames flicker through.

And she is swallow-fleet, and free
From mortal bonds and bars.
She laughs, because Eternity
Blossoms for her with stars!

O folk who scorn my stiff gray gown,
My dull and foolish face,
Can ye not see my Soul flash down,
A singing flame through space?

And folk, whose earth-stained looks I hate,
Why may I not divine
Your Souls, that must be passionate,
Shining, and swift as mine?

FANNIE STEARNS DAVIS

Here is a cheerful poem to remind us of something that we often forget. It takes a little shadow to make us remember the sun.

Shadows

A dark, elusive shadow—
   Trailing my pleasant way
Through thronging street, and meadow
   All on a summer's day.

But what care I for shadows!
   Of substance, they have none;
And he who casts the shadows
   Is walking in the sun!

ARTHUR J. PEEL

We all have our ups and downs, our golden days and our gray days. Don't you think that this poem expresses it beautifully? The last line is an especially "shining" one.

Days

Some days my thoughts are just cocoons—all cold,
    and dull, and blind,
They hang from branches in the gray woods
    of my mind;

And other days they drift and shine—such free
    and flying things!
I find the gold-dust in my hair, left by their brushing wings.

KARLE WILSON BAKER

People often do not realize how cruel gossip can be until it touches them. Have you ever been in a group when you held your breath lest something unkind be said about you or someone you love? It's a very unhappy feeling.

Gossip

Before I knew how cruel
   Just common talk can be,
I thought that words were singing things
   With colors like the sea.

But since I've felt their caustic lash,
   And know how they can sting,
I hold my breath when words go by
   For fear they will not sing.

LEXIE DEAN ROBERTSON

Have you ever passed an empty house and wondered who had lived in it or who was going to move in? Could you tell what kind of people had lived in the house—careful people or untidy people—children or grown-ups? There is one especially lovely stanza in this poem. Can you find it?

The House with Nobody in It

Whenever I walk to Suffern along the Erie track
I go by a poor old farmhouse with its shingles broken
    and black.
I suppose I've passed it a hundred times, but I always stop
    for a minute
And look at the house, the tragic house, the house with
    nobody in it.

I never have seen a haunted house, but I hear there are
    such things;
That they hold the talk of spirits, their mirth and
    sorrowings.
I know this house isn't haunted, and I wish it were, I do;
For it wouldn't be so lonely if it had a ghost or two.

This house on the road to Suffern needs a dozen
    panes of glass,
And somebody ought to weed the walk and take a scythe to
    the grass.

It needs new paint and shingles, and the vines should
    be trimmed and tied;
But what it needs the most of all is some people living inside.

If I had a lot of money and all my debts were paid
I'd put a gang of men to work with brush and saw and spade.
I'd buy that place and fix it up the way it used to be
And I'd find some people who wanted a home and give
    it to them free.

Now, a new house standing empty, with staring window
    and door,
Looks idle, perhaps, and foolish, like a hat on its block
    in the store.
But there's nothing mournful about it; it cannot be sad
    and lone
For the lack of something within it that it has never known.

But a house that has done what a house should do, a house
    that has sheltered life,
That has put its loving wooden arms around a man
    and his wife,
A house that has echoed a baby's laugh and held up his
    stumbling feet,
Is the saddest sight, when it's left alone, that ever your eyes
    could meet.

So whenever I go to Suffern along the Erie track
I never go by the empty house without stopping and
    looking back,
Yet it hurts me to look at the crumbling roof and the shutters
    fallen apart,
For I can't help thinking the poor old house is a house with a
    broken heart.

JOYCE KILMER

*Other people live now in the old stone quarters where
the slaves were kept, but perhaps their ghosts come
back and play the banjos once again when moonlight
fills the square.*

Slave Quarter

I can hear banjos
Soft and light
Down in the courtyard
In the moonlight.

What are they playing?
I cannot know,
For players and music
Died long ago.

CARL CARMER

The greatest blessing in the world is work. Few things are more difficult than to sit still and do nothing. Sometimes we are inclined to forget all this and complain because we have work to do. This poem should help to make us more cheerful and contented.

Work

Let me but do my work from day to day,
   In field or forest, at the desk or loom,
   In roaring market-place or tranquil room;
Let me but find it in my heart to say,
When vagrant wishes beckon me astray,
   "This is my work; my blessing, not my doom;
   Of all who live, I am the one by whom
This work can best be done in the right way."

Then shall I see it not too great, nor small,
   To suit my spirit and to prove my powers;
   Then shall I cheerful greet the labouring hours,
And cheerful turn, when the long shadows fall
At eventide, to play and love and rest,
Because I know for me my work is best.

HENRY VAN DYKE

Sometime when you want very much to have something that you ought to wait for until you are older, read this poem. It is very hard for parents to refuse what their children ask, but they do not want you to use up all the lovely experiences in life before you are old enough to enjoy or appreciate them. It is surprising how things lose their thrill as soon as we possess them.

I Bid You Keep
Some Few Small Dreams

I pray that you may never have
   The things you long for most,
For he who gratifies desire
   Must pay a princely cost.

The world was spread out at my feet;
   It spelled romance to me;
I spent ten years in travel—
   Now there's nothing left to see.

The doll I wanted as a child
   Seemed strangely wonderful,
Until I held her in my arms—
   Then she was just a doll.

The things we long for give to life
   The purpose and the gleam.
The things we get, however fine,
   Are never what they seem.

O rather would I bid you keep
   A few small dreams in trust,
Than see you have the things you want
   And watch them turn to dust.

                    HELEN FRAZEE-BOWER

There is a good deal to think about in this short poem. Why do you think that Courage should wear a crimson coat? Have you ever seen the cap and gown that Knowledge wears or the cloth of gold on some famous king or queen, either real or in the movies? Behind each one of them, however, there is usually some patient mother or sister or aunt weaving their fine robes out of her own self-sacrifice.

Courage Has a Crimson Coat

Courage has a crimson coat
   Trimmed with trappings bold,
Knowledge dons a dress of note,
   Fame's is cloth of gold.
Far they ride and fair they roam,
   Much they do and dare;
Gray-gowned Patience sits at home,
   And weaves the stuff they wear.

NANCY BYRD TURNER

Perhaps already you have heard the sound of a silver horn. Never let your ears grow dull to it; never let the love of money make you long for a golden pillow. The world will call you mad, but don't mind that. Study and work and serve and follow—follow the silver horn.

Madman's Song

Better to see your cheek grown hollow,
Better to see your temple worn,
Than to forget to follow, follow,
After the sound of a silver horn.

Better to bind your brow with willow
And follow, follow until you die,
Than to sleep with your head on a golden pillow,
Nor lift it up when the hunt goes by.

Better to see your cheek grown sallow
And your hair grown gray, so soon, so soon,
Than to forget to hallo, hallo,
After the milk-white hounds of the moon.

ELINOR WYLIE

*Here is a pretty problem. Why do you see a fool
when you look into a mirror and a wise man when
you see yourself in a pool?*

The Mirror

When I look into a glass
   Myself's my only care;
But I look into a pool
   For all the wonders there.

When I look into a glass
   I see a fool;
But I see a wise man
   When I look into a pool.

WILLIAM H. DAVIES

The word "prior" means first. What do you consider the prior claim upon your days? Is it the same for all persons or at all stages of our existence? What are some of the little unimportant time-wasting things that we do every day?

The Lien

Relentless press of little things;
Eternal haste to do them all;
The prior claim upon our days
Relinquished to the trivial.

Our obligations never paid,
But endless and imperative.
O Life, why must you always leave
So little time to live?

ADELAIDE LOVE

Many a good mechanic has been spoiled because his parents wanted him to be a doctor or a lawyer. That which is useful and serves mankind is also beautiful; so do not be ashamed to serve the world with your hands if that is your gift.

Misdirection

I shape the vessel of my life,
    Hammer it cold, hammer it hot.
I try my best to make of it
    What it is not.

Blow, bellows, blow;
    Burn, fire, burn—
I try to shape a silver vase
    Out of a copper urn.

ELEANOR SLATER

When you put money into a bank it is not always safe. You may have to spend it or robbers may steal it, but the coins which we put into our "heart's treasury" are safe forever. The memories of beautiful music, lovely poems, and wonderful pictures are coins of this kind. Can you think of others?

The Coin

Into my heart's treasury
   I slipped a coin
That time cannot take
   Nor thief purloin,—
Oh, better than the minting
   Of a gold-crowned king
Is the safe-kept memory
   Of a lovely thing.

SARA TEASDALE

INDEX
TO AUTHORS

INDEX
TO TITLES

INDEX
TO FIRST LINES